Complete EnglishSmart

Grade 4

Desmond Gilling • Kim Vicic

ISBN : 1–894810–67–8

Copyright © 2004 **Popular Book Company (Canada) Limited**

Printed in China

Complete EnglishSmart *Contents*

Integrated Practice

1 Ghosts

The idea of ghosts all around us is a scary <u>concept</u>. We picture <u>horrifying</u> shapes in <u>transparent</u> white sheets drifting above the ground making <u>eerie</u> sounds. But do ghosts actually exist? Do you believe in ghosts?

There are various types of ghosts according to ghost specialists. The most common type is the "crisis <u>apparition</u>". These ghosts represent dying persons and appear to close relatives. A "tape recording ghost" is a ghost that <u>reenacts</u> an action from their time period but does not react to the living. One man reported seeing soldiers march through his house with their legs below the floor. Apparently, these soldiers were walking on an <u>ancient</u> road that was below the floor level in the house. These ghosts were <u>oblivious</u> to the man and just walked right past him.

Some ghosts known as "cyclic ghosts" appear every year on the same day. Anne Boleyn, the beheaded wife of King Henry VIII, has been seen on December 24 in Hever Castle, Kent, her childhood home. She was seen carrying her head under her arm! Marilyn Monroe, the <u>legendary</u> movie star, has been seen on August 4, the day she died in 1962.

Poltergeists are troublesome ghosts. They often make loud noises, make objects fly across the rooms, and create <u>chaos</u>. Poltergeists may throw things around but they seldom hurt anyone. In one <u>documented</u> case, a poltergeist hurled a teapot across a room and just before it was to hit someone, it magically changed direction.

People troubled by ghosts can call "ghost hunters". They have special equipment to detect the presence of ghosts. In the 1984 film, "Ghostbusters", ghost hunters chased away ghosts with laser guns.

Recalling Facts - True or False

A. Place "T" for true or "F" for false beside each statement.

1. King Henry VIII's wife was beheaded. .... T

2. The ghost of Marilyn Monroe has been seen on the anniversary
   of her death. .... T

3. Poltergeists are happy, friendly ghosts. .... F

4. Poltergeists like to bother old people. .... F

5. It is rare for a poltergeist to actually harm anyone physically. .... F

6. If ghosts bother you, you can call a "ghost hunter". .... T

7. "Ghostbusters" is the name of an actual company. .... F

8. Some ghosts ignore human beings. .... T

B. Match the types of ghosts with the description. Place the letters in the circles provided.

1. A crisis apparition ghost (A)   A troublemaker (A)

2. A tape recording ghost (B)   B appears to relatives when at the point of death (F)

3. A cyclic ghost (C)   C acts out an action from a previous time (G)

4. A poltergeist (D)   D appears on the anniversary of its death (H)

Using Information

C. Answer the following questions in sentence form.

1. What evidence in the story suggests that ghosts probably do exist?

   _____

   _____

2. Which type of ghost do you think is the scariest? Give two reasons.

   _____

   _____

Nouns

- A Noun is a word that represents a person, a place, or a thing.
  - *Examples:* 1. Judy, Mark, girl, boy – are "person" nouns
    - 2. home, school, CN Tower, Canadian National Exhibition – are "place" nouns
    - 3. dog, bicycle, comb, radio – are "thing" nouns

D. Underline the word in each list that is not a noun.

1. car, Susan, cried, museum

2. England, Rome, tired, carpenter

3. Atlantic Ocean, ran, teacher, parents

4. find, clothing, hat, purse

5. behave, behaviour, student, test

6. walked, bookends, textbook, walkway

7. tears, years, fears, hears

8. delicious, cake, cookies, pie

Types of Nouns – Common and Proper

- A Proper Noun is a particular, unique person, place, or thing. A proper noun begins with a capital letter.
  - *Examples:* John, Chicago, Air Canada Centre, Maple Avenue Public School – these are all proper nouns because they refer to something specific.

- A Common Noun is a person, place, or thing that is part of a classification.
  - *Examples:* boy, city, arena, school – these are the same as the above except they are the general term for the proper nouns above.

E. Match the common nouns with the proper nouns.

Note that the common noun refers to the type of noun, while the proper noun refers to a specific person, place, or thing.

#		Common Noun			Letter	Proper Noun
1.	I	tower			A	Adam Sandler
2.	J	radio			B	The Dome
3.	K	school			C	Air Canada Centre
4.	L	arena			D	Walkman
5.	M	stadium			E	Britney Spears
6.	N	car			F	CN Tower
7.	O	singer			G	St. Joseph's High School
8.	P	actor			H	Toyota

Words in Context

- When we are trying to understand the meaning of a word that is new to us, it is helpful to read the word in its context. Context is the use of the word in a sentence that reveals its meaning.

F. **Match the underlined words in column A with the definitions in column B.**

In the reading passage, there are 11 underlined words that would be useful for you to know. Read the sentence in which each word appears and figure out its meaning.

Column A	Column B
1. concept	A confusion
2. horrifying	B old
3. transparent	C vision
4. eerie	D unaware
5. apparition	E famous
6. reenacts	F terrifying
7. ancient	G see-through
8. oblivious	H idea
9. legendary	I recorded
10. chaos	J strange
11. documented	K repeats

G. **Choose any five words from column A and use them in a sentence of your own to show that you understand their meanings.**

1. _the idea fo the is._

2. _there is 2 tipision fo that eerie sound._

3. _____

4. _____

5. _____

The Human Heart

The heart is a powerful <u>involuntary</u> muscle that sends blood throughout our body. We cannot control what it does and we cannot stop it from beating. The heart sends a single drop of blood around the 100,000 kilometres of blood vessels about a thousand times a day. This is an <u>incredible</u> feat for a muscle that is the size of a human fist.

The heart is made up of four <u>chambers</u> – two at the top and two at the bottom. At the top, the left atrium and the right atrium collect the blood and the bottom two chambers, the ventricles, pump the blood out of the heart. The blood begins in the right atrium. Once this atrium is filled, the blood is squeezed down into the right ventricle where it is sent to the lungs. In the lungs, the blood loads up on oxygen and then enters the heart again through the left atrium. It then passes down to the left ventricle where it is then sent all over the body. Incredibly, all this happens in one single heartbeat.

To ensure that the blood travels smoothly and <u>consistently</u>, the heart uses valves that open and shut with the flow of blood. The valves only open one way making sure that blood does not re-enter the chambers. A doctor using a stethoscope can hear both the heartbeat and the sound of the <u>valves</u> shutting tightly.

When you are ready for physical action such as running, your heart speeds up and delivers large amounts of oxygen to your legs <u>enabling</u> you to run quickly. After exercising, you may feel <u>exhausted</u> as your oxygen reserve may be used up. In a few moments, however, you will recover the oxygen needed at rest and your heart will slow down and <u>resume</u> a normal rate. The <u>typical</u> heart rate of an adult is 60 – 80 beats per minute while a younger heart would beat at a rate of 80 –100 beats per minute.

Recalling Details

A. Circle the letters of the correct answers.

1. The job of the heart is to
   - A. send blood throughout the body.
   - B. fill blood with oxygen.
   - C. help us run quickly.
   - D. send blood to the lungs.

2. The size of the human heart is about
   - A. the same size as our head.
   - B. the size of a fist.
   - C. the size of a baseball.
   - D. 5 cm in height and 2 cm in width.

3. To make sure that blood circulates smoothly, the heart uses
   - A. a pacemaker.
   - B. blood vessels.
   - C. valves that open and shut.
   - D. oxygen.

4. The valves control
   - A. heartbeat.
   - B. the amount of blood flow.
   - C. the direction of blood flow.
   - D. the amount of oxygen in the blood.

5. To listen to your heartbeat, a doctor uses
   - A. a kaleidoscope.
   - B. a stethoscope.
   - C. a microscope.
   - D. a telescope.

6. When you are ready for physical action, your heart delivers
   - A. oxygen to your muscles.
   - B. electricity to your lungs.
   - C. blood to your feet.
   - D. air to your lungs.

Matching the Facts

B. Match the facts.

1. ventricles
2. 60 – 80 beats
3. 4 chambers
4. involuntary
5. 80 – 100 beats
6. open one way only

A adult's heart rate
B the atriums and the ventricles
C type of muscle
D the valves to prevent re-entry of blood
E pump blood out of the heart
F child's heart rate

Verbs

- A Verb is an action word that tells what the subject is doing. It can also describe a state of being.
  Examples (action): *walk, run, jump, fly, sing, dance, scream are all action verbs.*
- A non-action verb gives the state of the noun.
  Examples (non-action): *am, is, was, are, were*

C. Underline the verb(s) in each sentence and in the space provided write "A" for action word(s) and "N" for non-action word(s).

1. The children played in the park. .... ☐

2. The birds flew high above the trees. .... ☐

3. He is nine years old. .... ☐

4. Where were you last night? .... ☐

5. What time is it? .... ☐

6. The girls sang in the choir. .... ☐

7. He was the first to arrive. .... ☐

8. Do not cross the street without looking both ways. .... ☐

9. The pupils studied for the test and they scored high marks. .... ☐

10. She is shy sometimes but she is also comical. .... ☐

No. 9 and No.10 each have 2 verbs.

D. Fill in the blanks with the appropriate verbs provided.

> sailed   built   took   went   stayed   flew   camped

During the summer holidays, many students 1._____ on

vacation. John 2._____ to England to visit his relatives. Susan

3._____ her uncle's boat. Paul 4._____ in the woods

with his parents and 5._____ a campfire every night. Some pupils

6._____ home. They 7._____ day trips to various places.

Synonym Crossword Puzzle

E. Use the clues to complete the crossword puzzle. The words are underlined in the reading passage.

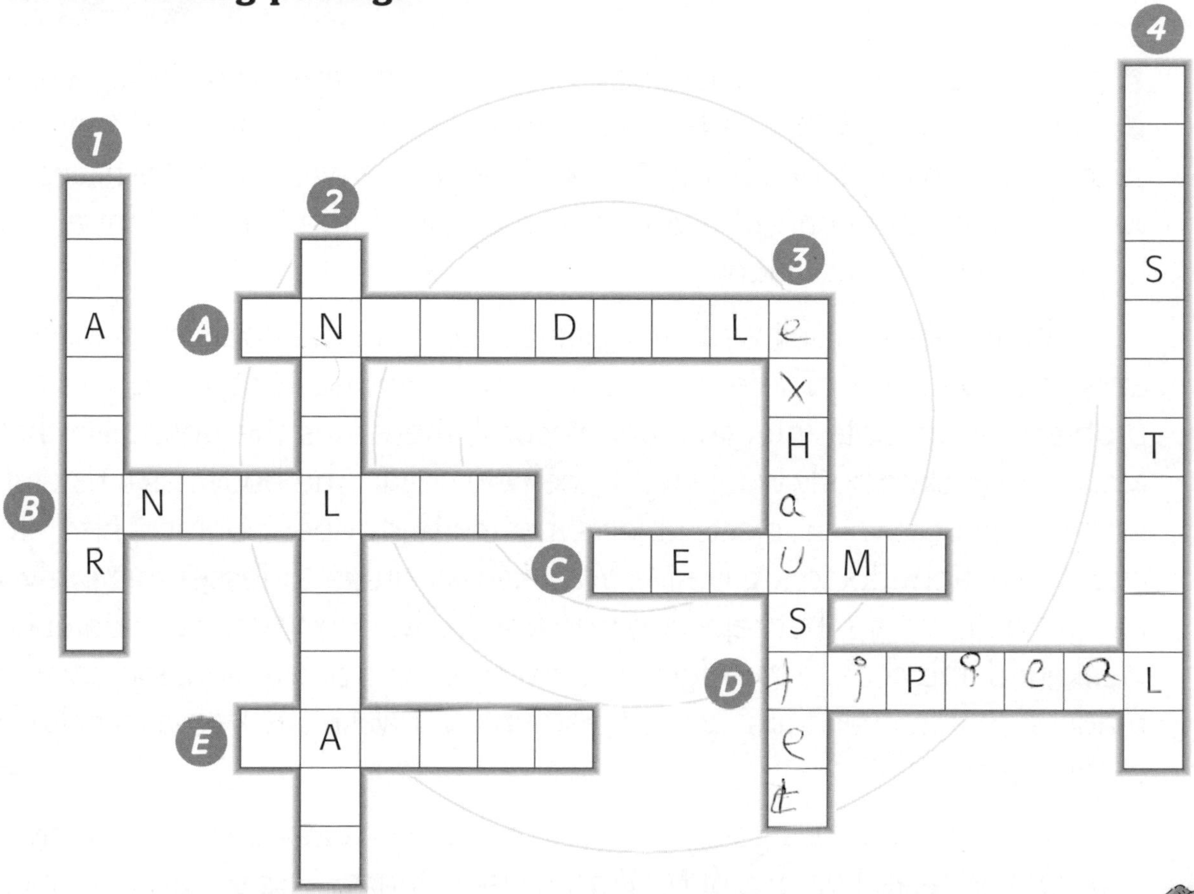

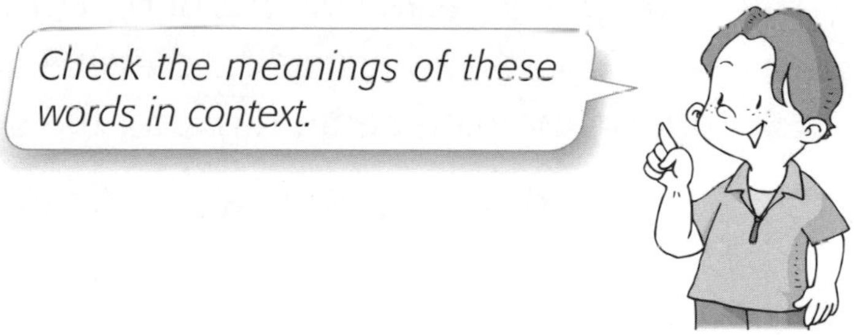
Check the meanings of these words in context.

Down

1. rooms to store blood
2. acts on its own
3. tired
4. regularly, always the same

Across

A. unbelievable
B. giving it the power
C. continue
D. usual
E. parts of the heart that open and shut

The First Heart Transplant

In December, 1967, in Groote Schuur Hospital in Capetown, South Africa, medical history was made. Dr. Christian Barnard performed the first successful transplant of a human heart. The patient was Louis Washkansky, who received the heart of a young woman killed in a car accident a few hours before the operation.

The transplant itself was traumatic, but so were the hours immediately after the operation. There were two main concerns. First, there was the problem of possible infection, and second, there was the possibility that Mr. Washkansky's body would reject the new heart. The body has a natural, built-in defence which rejects objects that the body does not recognize. To avoid rejection, doctors gave Mr. Washkansky drugs to lessen his body's natural defence so that rejection was less likely. However, with defence weakened, the chance for infection increased. As a precaution, the doctors made sure that everything near and around Mr. Washkansky, was sterilized or disinfected.

The transplant was going very well for the first two weeks. Suddenly a dark spot appeared on one of Mr. Washkansky's lungs. This signalled trouble. Dr. Barnard and his staff did everything possible to save Mr. Washkansky, but on the nineteenth day after the operation, he died.

Although Mr. Washkansky did not survive the transplant, the operation was considered a success. It paved the way for many more attempts to follow. Today, heart transplants are performed regularly. Many of those who were born with congenital heart conditions and doomed to die at an early age now live long and healthy lives. Thanks to the pioneering efforts of Dr. Christian Barnard.

Fact or Opinion

- A *Fact* refers to information that is given exactly from the passage. An *Opinion* is your interpretation of the information in the passage.

A. For each statement below, place "F" for fact or "O" for opinion in the space provided.

1. A heart transplant is a delicate operation. .... ☐

2. The first transplant made medical history. .... ☐

3. Mr. Washkansky received a healthy heart. .... ☐

4. The transplanted heart came from a car accident victim. .... ☐

5. Everyone was worried about the time after the operation. .... ☐

6. The possibility of infection was a major concern. .... ☐

7. Rejection of the new heart was a possibility. .... ☐

8. The drugs given to Mr. Washkansky were risky. .... ☐

9. Everything around Mr. Washkansky had to be sterilized. .... ☐

10. The first few weeks after a transplant is a dangerous time. .... ☐

11. The transplant operation was a success even though the patient died. .... ☐

12. It is much safer to have a heart transplant today. .... ☐

13. Congenital heart problems are serious. .... ☐

14. Dr. Barnard is a hero. .... ☐

Your Opinion

B. Write a response to each question giving your point of view.

1. Was Dr. Barnard a hero in the medical community? Give reasons.

   _____

   _____

2. How do you think Mr. Washkansky felt immediately after having transplant?

   _____

The Basic Sentence

- A Basic Sentence is made up of two parts: the Subject and the Predicate.
- The subject contains a noun that performs the action in the sentence or is the thing being described by the predicate.

Example: The children laughed out loud at the joke.
The subject is "the children"; the predicate is "laughed out loud at the joke".

C. Draw a vertical line separating the subject and the predicate in each sentence below.

1. He played with his dog in the backyard.

2. His parents told him to be home by 4:30.

3. His birthday presents were hidden under the bed.

4. Melanie's best friend is Sandra.

5. Two and two make four.

6. They played hide-and-seek in the old house.

D. Match the subjects with the appropriate predicates.

Subject	Predicate
1. The ballerina	A. won all their games.
2. Both his parents	B. often get injured.
3. The school team	C. sat in the cockpit.
4. Professional athletes	D. had to be on her toes.
5. The pilot	E. went to work each day.

E. Construct sentences using the words provided as subjects and predicates.

1. (players, won) _____

2. (dogs, cat, chased) _____

3. (sun, rose) _____

4. (laughed, children) _____

Words Often Confused

F. **Below are groups of words that are often confused because they look alike or sound similar. Circle the words that match the meanings.**

1.	its / it's	belongs to it
2.	they're / there / their	belongs to them
3.	here / hear	a place
4.	diary / dairy	buy milk there
5.	feet / feat	an accomplishment
6.	forth / fourth	place in a race
7.	duel / dual	two of them
8.	whether / weather	condition outside
9.	to / too / two	also
10.	loose / lose	doesn't fit
11.	dessert / desert	pie or cake
12.	clothes / cloths	material

Use a dictionary to check the meanings and avoid confusion.

G. **Use the following words to make sentences to show their meanings.**

1. diary   – _____

2. duel   – _____

3. whether – _____

4. desert   – _____

5. forth   – _____

6. lose   – _____

The Incredible Butterfly

Butterflies are among nature's most beautiful creations. While their colours have always been admired, particularly by artists, they serve other purposes. Some butterflies use their colour for camouflage. They are able to blend in with tree branches or flowers that they feed on. Some butterflies use their bright colouring as a warning to predators. The Magnificent Owl butterfly has a large dot on its wing that looks exactly like an owl's eye. This tricks predators into thinking that the butterfly is a larger animal.

Most butterflies feed on the nectar of plants. They use a long mouth part called a proboscis to dip into the flowers and suck up the nectar. Some butterflies prefer to feed on rotting fruit. Butterflies are important to nature because they pollinate plants when they feed.

During its lifecycle, a butterfly goes through many changes in both body form and colour. There are four stages of butterfly life: egg, caterpillar (larva), chrysalis (pupa), and adult. After about two weeks, baby caterpillars hatch from eggs and start feeding. This stage lasts anywhere from 3 to 12 weeks, depending on the species. The pupa stage is where the caterpillar changes into a butterfly. This transformation takes about two weeks.

Butterflies are found all over the world, but the widest diversity of the species is found in tropical climates. The most familiar butterfly to North Americans is the Monarch butterfly.

Using Information

A. **Write short answers to the following questions using information from the reading passage above.**

1. Why do artists in particular like butterflies?

_____

2. How are butterflies important to nature?

    _____

3. How do butterflies defend themselves against predators?

    _____

B. Rearrange the four lifecycle changes of the butterfly to the order in which they occur.

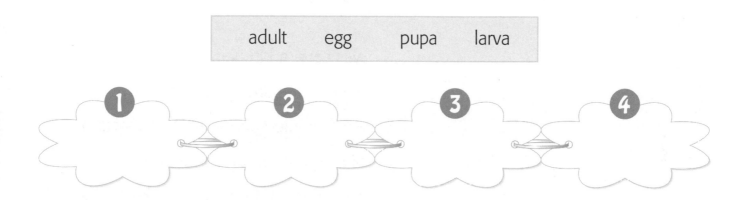

| adult | egg | pupa | larva |

Further Facts

C. Fill in the blanks with the proper words provided.

| world | Magnificent Owl | | flowers |
| pupa | nectar | Monarch | proboscis |

Butterflies feed on the 1._____ of plants. They are equipped with a

2._____ which dips into the 3._____ to get food. Caterpillars

become butterflies in the 4._____ stage. Butterflies are found all over the

5._____. The 6._____ butterfly has a large dot on its wing.

The 7._____ butterfly is most familiar to North Americans.

Building Simple Sentences

D. **Each sentence below is missing a subject. Provide a suitable subject for each and write it in the space provided. Try to include descriptive words to suit the predicate meaning.**

> **Example:** The excited boy jumped up and down. The word "excited" helps explain why the boy (subject) jumped up and down.

1. _____ was covered in paint.

2. _____ went to the shopping mall.

3. _____ were worried about the Math test.

4. _____ built a tree fort all on his own.

5. _____ flew over the fence and broke a window.

6. _____ seldom shared his candy.

7. _____ came first in the race.

8. _____ arrived in Canada for the first time.

E. **Compose a predicate ending for each of the incomplete sentences below. Try to include descriptive details.**

1. The fearless firefighter _____.

2. The playful kitten _____.

3. The entire school _____.

4. The sad little boy _____.

5. The entire audience _____.

6. All the fans _____.

7. Most of the players on the team _____.

8. All of my friends _____.

Root Words and Building New Words

F. Below is a list of root words that have been changed to make new words in the passage. Write the new word from the passage beside its root word.

1. transform _____   2. warn _____

3. create _____   4. wide _____

5. diverse _____   6. tropics _____

7. beauty _____   8. depend _____

G. Fill in the chart below creating new words from the words given. A prefix is given for the first new word and a suffix for the second.

	WORD	1st NEW WORD		2nd NEW WORD	
1.	change	ex		able	
2.	print	im		ing	
3.	polite	im		ness	
4.	believe	dis		able	
5.	patient	im		ce	
6.	real	un		istic	
7.	definite	in		ly	
8.	behave	mis		iour	
9.	appoint	dis		ment	
10.	sincere	in		ity	

Words can be altered by adding a prefix or a suffix or by changing the form of the word.

The Atlas

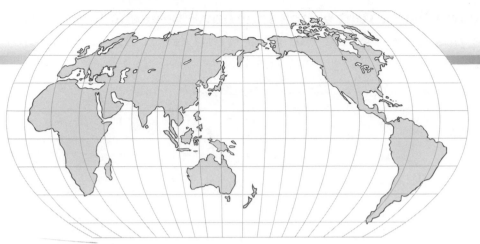

An atlas is a scale model of the earth. It helps us look at the entire earth or large sections of the earth's surface. There are seven large land masses called continents that make up the earth's surface. These include: Africa, Asia, South America, North America, Europe, Antarctica, and Australasia. The water surface of the earth is divided into five oceans: Atlantic, Pacific, Indian, Arctic, and Antarctic.

To help us find locations on the globe, there are lines called grids that run in east-west and north-south directions. These lines are often referred to as lines of latitude and longitude. The imaginary line that circles the globe halfway between the North Pole and the South Pole is called the equator. A similar imaginary circle that runs north-south and passes through Greenwich is called the prime meridian. Lines of latitude (called parallels because they run parallel to the equator) run east-west and measure distances north and south of the equator. Lines of longitude (called meridians) run north-south and measure distances east and west of the prime meridian.

Distances on an atlas are measured in degree (°). Degrees are further divided into minutes. There are 60 minutes for each degree. The equator is at 0° while the North Pole is at 90°. Therefore, the distance from the North Pole to the South Pole is 180° in total. Similarly, the prime meridian is at 0° and distances east and west are between 0° and 180° in both directions for a total of 360° (180° E and 180° W). Therefore, it is easy to plot an exact location on a map. Toronto, for example, is at roughly 80° west of the prime meridian and 45° north of the equator.

Recalling Details

A. **Match the facts from column A with the meanings in column B.**

Column A		Column B
1. continents ☐		A oceans
2. degrees ☐		B located at 0° longitude
3. 60 ☐		C run parallel to the equator
4. 7 of these ☐		D minutes for each degree
5. longitude & latitude ☐		E measurement of longitude & latitude
6. equator ☐		F continents
7. meridians ☐		G land masses
8. 5 of these ☐		H east-west/north-south lines
9. parallels ☐		I run parallel to the prime meridian
10. prime meridian ☐		J located at 0° latitude

Content Quiz

B. **Can you list the oceans of the world?**

1. ☐   2. ☐   3. ☐

4. ☐   5. ☐

C. **Underline the seven continents. Be careful – some of these are countries, not continents.**

New Zealand   Australasia   Venezuela   Australia   United States

Central America   China   Asia   Europe   Holland   Canada   Africa

South America   North America   Mexico   Antarctica

Adjectives and Adverbs

- We use Adjectives to describe nouns and Adverbs to describe verbs.

  The underlined words are all adjectives which describe the nouns that follow them: the <u>little</u> boy, the <u>scary</u> story, the <u>tall</u> building, the <u>happy</u> child, the <u>fast</u> runner, the <u>slippery</u> steps, the <u>dark</u> hallway, the <u>loud</u> crash

D. Find the nouns in the following sentences and underline the adjectives that describe them. The number following each sentence tells you how many adjectives to find.

1. The excited children make for a loud party. (2)

2. The tall, husky man lifted the heavy furniture. (3)

3. When the tired boy arrived home, he jumped into his warm bed. (2)

4. The expensive watch was found in the top drawer of the antique dresser. (3)

5. The shiny new red bicycle was the perfect birthday gift. (5)

The subject word in a sentence is not always the only noun. Remember – a noun is any person, place, or thing.

E. Underline the adverbs in the following sentences. The number following each sentence tells you how many adverbs to find.

1. The athlete competed gallantly for the championship. (1)

2. She played bravely and courageously but lost the competition. (2)

3. He moved silently and quickly like a cat. (2)

4. He had never seen such a sight. (1)

5. The horse leaped proudly and brilliantly over the pond. (2)

The underlined words are all adverbs which describe the verbs next to them: ran <u>slowly</u>, swam <u>quickly</u>, jumped <u>high</u>, spoke <u>clearly</u>, laughed <u>hysterically</u>, tried <u>desperately</u>. Note: adverbs often end in "ly" and they answer the questions "how", "where", "how often" and "when".

New Word Scramble

F. The following scrambled words are from the reading passage. Use the definition clue to unscramble each of the words.

1.	ginyraami	i	m	a	g	i	n	a	r	y		unreal, in your mind
2.	rotquea	e	q	u	a		o					the line at 0° latitude
3.	retine	e	n	t	i	r	e					the whole thing
4.	dirsg		g	r	i	d	s					lines on the globe
5.	riccles	c	i	r	c	l	e	s				goes round
6.	ceaxt		e	x	a	c	t					precise, accurate
7.	lasec		c	l	a	s	e					the same but much smaller
8.	mirep		p	r	i	m	e					first, most important
9.	dutelati	l	a	t	i	t	u	d	e			also called parallel
10.	censtios	s	e	c	t	i	o	n	s			parts, pieces of

Challenge – Using New Words in Sentences

G. Compose five sentences by using two words from the scramble list above in each sentence.

1. _____

_____

2. _____

_____

3. _____

_____

4. _____

_____

5. _____

_____

6 Disasters at Sea (1)

While the sinking of the Titanic is the most famous shipwreck of all time, there are numerous other marine tragedies. The sinking of the Empress of Ireland, the Britannic, and the Lusitania are other notable disasters at sea.

On April 10, 1912, the Titanic departed on her maiden voyage from Southampton, England heading across the Atlantic to New York City. The Titanic was the most luxurious passenger liner of its time. The 2,227 passengers were to enjoy the many luxuries of the Titanic, which included a gymnasium, a heated swimming pool, elegant dining rooms, stately passenger rooms, and a grand ballroom.

Four days after leaving Southampton, at approximately 11:39 p.m., a lookout by the name of Frederick Fleet spotted an iceberg approaching out of the fog. A minute later, the iceberg struck the hull of the Titanic causing severe damage. In less than three hours, the ship split in two and the bow plunged into the sea.

The ship was not equipped with enough lifeboats to carry all the passengers. When the ship was going down, many passengers were left helplessly floating in the dark, cold waters of the Atlantic. Over 1,500 died that fateful night.

Just two years after the Titanic tragedy, the Empress of Ireland, another upscale passenger ship, sank in the St. Lawrence River just east of Quebec City. In the early morning, May 29, 1914, a Norwegian coal ship, the Storstad, rammed the Empress of Ireland in thick fog. It took only 14 minutes for the liner to sink. Over 1,000 passengers never made it out of their beds. Those who plunged into the water either drowned or died of hypothermia. Of the 1,477 passengers on board the Empress, 1,012 died.

Recalling Facts – True or False

A.   Place "T" for true or "F" for false beside each statement.

1.   The Titanic left New York City on April 10, 1912. .... ☐

2.   Most of the passengers on the Titanic were poor immigrants. .... ☐

3.   There were 2,227 passengers aboard the Titanic. .... ☐

4.   The Titanic was struck by another ship. .... ☐

5.   The Titanic was a luxurious ocean liner. .... ☐

6.   Frederick Fleet was the captain of the Titanic. .... ☐

7.   The Titanic did not have enough lifeboats. .... ☐

8.   Over 1,500 Titanic passengers and crew died. .... ☐

9.   The Empress of Ireland also sank in the Atlantic Ocean. .... ☐

10.   The Empress of Ireland was struck by another ship. .... ☐

11.   The Empress of Ireland took less than 15 minutes to sink. .... ☐

12.   More passengers on the Empress of Ireland died than on the Titanic. .... ☐

Using Facts – Your Opinion

B.   Answer the following question with your opinion based on the facts of the story.

How was the Titanic poorly prepared for emergency? What extra precautions should have been made?

_____

_____

_____

_____

_____

Constructing Simple Sentences

C. Use each group of words to construct a sentence.

Example: the, around, dog, the, chased, cat, room, the

The dog chased the cat around the room.

Try and find the verb first. Then build the sentence.

1. hockey the watched game parents their play children

_____

2. candles the cake had nine it on birthday

_____

3. son fishing his went and the lake in father the

_____

4. ended school began when holidays summer the

_____

Using Adverbs and Adjectives

D. For the passage below, fill in the blanks with adverbs and adjectives to make it more interesting. Remember – adverbs often end in "ly".

Because it was a 1._____ summer day, James and Philip ran

2._____ to the 3._____ swimming pool and jumped into the

4._____ water. The 5._____ lifeguard told them not to play

6._____ in case there was an accident. Once they had cooled off

7._____ , they went to buy a 8._____ ice-cream cone. They

ate their cones 9._____ and decided that they would swim

10._____ during the summer.

Descriptive Language

E. **In the reading passage, there are many descriptive words. For each of the following eight words from the passage, underline the best synonym from the choices provided.**

1.	numerous	few many numbered luttered
2.	tragedies	incidents occurrences disasters events
3.	departed	arrived left dropped flew
4.	luxurious	expensive cheap nice important
5.	elegant	fancy neat tidy shiny
6.	grand	small loud large necessary
7.	rammed	struck jumped bumped touched
8.	upscale	luxurious high smaller similar

F. **Pretend that you are a reporter giving an account of the sinking of the Titanic. Write your radio broadcast below.**

Use as many of the new words above as you can. The first sentence is the beginning of your announcement.

This is _____ of WEBK Radio. I am reporting live from the scene of the sinking of the Titanic.

_____

_____

_____

_____

_____

Disasters at Sea (2)

A year after the Titanic tragedy, another luxury liner, the Lusitania, was to meet the same fate. The Lusitania transported passengers from North America to Ireland. Although it was a British ship, many of the passengers were American citizens. In 1914, a war broke out between the British and the Germans. The Germans warned that any ship flying a British flag could be destroyed on the seas. However, the passengers aboard the Lusitania did not believe that the German Navy would attack an unarmed passenger ship.

On May 7, 1915, off the southern coast of Ireland, a German submarine fired on the Lusitania. The torpedo struck the ship. The time from the torpedo hit to the complete sinking of the ship took only 18 minutes. Of the 1,959 people on board, only 764 survived. The American government was furious over the attack. Shortly afterwards, the Americans entered World War I to fight against the Germans.

The Britannic was a hospital ship and according to the rules of war, it was to be safe from attack. Built to be even more luxurious than the Titanic, it was converted to a hospital ship to service the soldiers of World War I. The Britannic was built to withstand the disastrous collision that sank the Titanic. However, on November 21, 1916, while cruising in the Mediterranean Sea, it either hit a German mine or was struck by a torpedo that exploded into her hull. It took 55 minutes for the Britannic to sink, giving time for many passengers to abandon ship. Luckily, the Mediterranean waters were calm and warm.

The Titanic, the Lusitania, and the Britannic were all closely related in both structure and purpose. Sadly, they all suffered the same fate.

Understanding the Main Idea of a Paragraph

• *The Main Idea of a paragraph is the basic topic being discussed.*

A. **Choose the statement that gives the main idea of each paragraph below by placing a check mark in the space provided.**

Paragraph One

1. _____ Germany was at war with Britain.

2. _____ The Lusitania travelled across the Atlantic Ocean.

3. _____ The Germans issued a warning to all English ships.

Paragraph Two

1. _____ The Lusitania was sunk by a German submarine.

2. _____ Only 764 of the 1,959 people on board survived.

3. _____ The Americans fought against the Germans in World War I.

Paragraph Three

1. _____ The Britannic was a luxurious hospital ship.

2. _____ The Britannic was thought to be safer than the Titanic.

3. _____ A German mine or a torpedo struck the Britannic and sank it.

 Comparison Chart

B. **Complete the chart to compare the Lusitania and the Britannic.**

	Lusitania	Britannic
1. Date of sinking	_____	_____
2. Type of ship	_____	_____
3. How it was attacked	_____	_____
4. Time it took to sink	_____	_____

Pronouns

- A Pronoun is used in place of a noun. It must agree in gender (male or female) and number with the word it is replacing.

  Singular Pronouns:

  my   mine   me   she   he   you   it   its   him   hers   his   you   your   yours

  Plural Pronouns:

  we   they   you   us   our   ours   your   yours   them   their   theirs

C. Choose the appropriate pronouns to replace the nouns.

> To help you, the noun has been underlined in each sentence.

1. <u>John</u> waited _____ turn in line.

2. <u>Sharon</u> bought _____ clothes at the department store.

3. Gregory and Sam called on <u>John</u> and asked if _____ could play.

4. The <u>children</u> washed _____ hands before eating _____ lunch.

5. <u>We</u> let <u>them</u> use _____ car because _____ broke down.

6. <u>We</u> bought _____ tickets for the <u>show</u> early because we didn't want to miss _____ .

7. When the new <u>students</u> arrived, the teacher asked us to help _____ .

Interrogative Pronouns

- Interrogative Pronouns ask questions. "Who", "what", "whom", "which", and "whose" are examples of interrogative pronouns.

D. Place the appropriate interrogative pronoun in each space provided.

1. _____ of the cars is the most expensive?

2. _____ will be joining us for dinner?

3. _____ house is this?

4. _____ are you doing this evening?

5. _____ student will be chosen to give a speech?

Descriptive Language – Building Vocabulary with Synonyms

- A Synonym is a word that has the same meaning as another word and could be used in place of that word.

E. Substitute the underlined word in each sentence with an appropriate synonym from the list below.

swiftly	elated	excited	exotic	chilly
delicious	elegant	modern	frosty	grand
scrumptious	depressing	drenched	spacious	soaked
	sentimental	constantly	frequently	

1. The rooms in the house were <u>big</u>. _____

2. Her dress was <u>nice</u>. _____

3. The food was <u>good</u>. _____

4. She talked <u>often</u>. _____

5. Her clothes were <u>wet</u>. _____

6. The dessert was <u>tasty</u>. _____

7. The children were <u>happy</u>. _____

8. It was a <u>sad</u> movie. _____

9. It was a <u>cold</u> night. _____

10. He ran <u>fast</u>. _____

F. Choose four of the words in the list and write a sentence for each showing its meaning.

1. _____

2. _____

3. _____

4. _____

Education in the Renaissance

Imagine that at one time a person could graduate from university without learning to read or write. In the Renaissance Period (1500-1650), people became interested in higher education. They wanted to learn the ancient languages such as Greek and Latin, and study mathematics, science and philosophy. Many universities were founded during the 16th century.

University education was a privilege of the rich. Girls were not allowed to attend and poor people could not afford to go. A member of a wealthy family could attend university at the age of ten. He might study at various universities and since the teaching was all done in Latin, it didn't matter in which country he studied. It was not unusual for a young boy to study one year in Italy and another in France without speaking either French or Italian.

It was possible in the 16th century to complete university without learning how to read or write. Since books were handwritten, there was not enough to give one to each student. Often, only the teacher had a book. He would read to the students who would memorize what he said. Tests were oral not written. In fact, many students finished school without ever writing a word!

For the not so wealthy, grammar schools were established in towns. They learned basic grammar and mathematics, and took part in bible study. At home, girls learned sewing, cooking, dancing, and the basics of taking care of a household. Poor children never attended school.

The Renaissance was a time when scholars did not simply accept what they were told. They conducted scientific experiments in search of answers to the mysteries of the universe. Copernicus calculated that the earth revolved around the sun but was afraid to publish his works for fear that the Church would punish him. Galileo later supported this theory. The watch, the telescope, and the submarine were some inventions of this period.

Making Inferences

- *An Inference is an idea you get from the information provided in the reading passage that you believe could be factual or true.*

A. **For each question below, give your answer based on the information you have read in the passage.**

1. If it was possible to graduate from university during the Renaissance without having learned how to read or write, how and what did pupils learn?

   _____

   _____

   _____

2. Why were girls not allowed to go to university during the Renaissance Period?

   _____

   _____

   _____

3. Why could the Renaissance be called "a period of curiosity"?

   _____

   _____

   _____

4. Why was Copernicus afraid that the Church would punish him for publishing his ideas about the universe?

   _____

   _____

   _____

The Direct Object

- A Direct Object in a sentence is the noun that receives the action of the verb.

  Example: *John kicked the soccer ball into the net.*

  In this case, the object would be the "ball" since it is the noun receiving the action of the verb "kicked".

  Note: the subject of the verb is "John" because he is performing the action of the verb "kicked".

B. Underline the direct objects in the sentences below.

One sentence has two direct objects.

1. Bill took his brother to the baseball game.

2. Paul lifted the cabinet by himself.

3. The girls played tennis in the morning.

4. Don't wake me up.

5. The teacher collected the test papers.

6. The police officer arrested the thief.

7. The plane carried the passengers across the ocean.

8. In the morning, they ate breakfast and went to school.

9. She ironed her dress and polished her shoes.

10. The sun broke through the clouds and warmed the flowers.

C. Complete each sentence by placing a direct object following the verb.

1. The students in the school enjoyed _____ .

2. To make the room tidy, they cleaned _____ .

3. Her mother baked _____ .

4. The boys in the band played _____ .

5. The talented carpenter built _____ .

Descriptive Language – Similes

- A Simile is a descriptive comparison between two objects that have similar qualities. These two objects are linked by the words "like" or "as".

  Example: He ran like the wind.
  Here the movement of running is compared to the movement of the wind.

- Often, animals and nature are used to form similes.

D. Complete the following simile comparisons.

1. He was as tall as _____ .

2. She jumped like _____ .

3. The moon shone like _____ .

4. He skated like _____ .

5. The plane flew like _____ .

6. The house was as large as _____ .

7. She laughed like _____ .

8. His stomach growled like _____ .

9. The baby was as playful as _____ .

10. He was as happy as _____ .

E. Create the first part of the simile for each description below.

1. She was as _____ as a lamb.

2. He was as _____ as an ox.

3. She _____ like a frog.

4. He _____ like a deer.

5. She _____ like a fish.

Plants – Nature's Medicine

Ancient civilizations discovered by experimenting that <u>certain</u> plants contained remedies to <u>illness</u>. They also discovered that some plants contained poisons that were often fatal. Once discovered, plants that were <u>medicinal</u> were cultivated in special gardens. This was the origin of herbal medicine as we know it today.

There are a number of plants that produce medicines that are used today. One of the most <u>popular</u> natural medicines in wide use today is ginseng, an ancient Chinese herbal remedy, that dates back 5,000 years. The leaves of the foxglove plant produce digitalis, which is used to treat heart conditions. It <u>helps</u> the heart beat <u>slower</u> and more regularly. The bark of the South American cinchona tree gives us quinine used to treat malaria. Quinine is also used to make tonic water. Hundreds of years ago, South American Indians discovered that chewing the leaves of the coca plant relieved pain. These leaves contain cocaine, which, in controlled doses, can be a <u>valuable</u> anaesthetic, but in large doses can be <u>deadly</u>. The deadly nightshade plant, also known as Belladonna, <u>produces</u> a drug known as atropine. This drug is used to treat stomach ailments and is also used in eye surgery. The opium poppy produces opium, which is turned into morphine, codeine and heroine. These drugs act as pain killers when given by doctors but can be deadly if taken without control.

Some plants are used for topical treatments. The term "topical" refers to use on the outside of the body, typically on the skin. Two of the most popular plants are aloe vera and jojoba. The creams produced from these plants are sold at cosmetic counters around the world. They are believed to reduce dryness and skin damage from sunburn.

Like our <u>ancient</u> ancestors, we are discovering the <u>benefits</u> of natural medicines in our everyday life. Creams, herbal teas, and food additives are some of the <u>common</u> uses today of the plant medicines.

Recalling Factual Information

A. Match the facts from the reading passage with the definitions.

1. herbal medicine ☐   A   common use today as herbal remedies

2. ginseng ☐   B   skin creams are made from these

3. foxglove plant ☐   C   chew these to relieve pain

4. cinchona tree ☐   D   also known as Deadly Nightshade

5. coca leaves ☐   E   produces powerful drugs for killing pain

6. Belladonna ☐   F   Chinese herbal remedy

7. opium poppy ☐   G   digitalis (heart drug) is made from this

8. topical ☐   H   produces quinine for curing malaria

9. aloe vera/jojoba ☐   I   general term for plants used as medicine

10. creams & herbal teas ☐   J   refers to outside the body

Reviewing Exact Details

B. Place "T" for true or "F" for false beside each statement.

1. Plant creams are sold at cosmetic counters. ☐

2. No plants contain poison. ☐

3. Ginseng is a recent discovery in plant medicine. ☐

4. Cocaine is used as an anaesthetic. ☐

5. Medicinal plants were grown in special gardens. ☐

6. Atropine is used to treat headaches. ☐

7. Morphine, the pain killer, is produced from opium. ☐

8. The cinchona tree is native to North America. ☐

9. Jojoba cream is good for the skin. ☐

10. Ancient civilizations discovered the use of plants as medicines. ☐

The Indirect Object

- The Indirect Object is the person or thing to or for which the action of the verb is done.

  Example: He gave me the money.
  The direct object is "money" and the indirect object is "me".

C. Underline the indirect object in each of the following sentences.

1.   She gave me the instructions.

2.   Paul sent his mother flowers on Mother's Day.

3.   Linda passed Cathy the ball.

4.   The teacher asked the pupils a difficult question.

5.   The father handed his son the tools he needed.

6.   She called her sister to come in for dinner.

7.   They asked us for directions to the highway.

8.   We sent him the money in an envelope.

9.   The man paid the mechanic $100.

10. Give him a call if you want to get a ride to school.

Subject, Direct Object, & Indirect Object

D. For each case, use the given words to compose a sentence that has each of the parts of speech above.

1.   offered   him   ride

_____

2.   letter   sent   her

_____

3.   father   asked   reason

_____

Antonyms

- *Antonyms, unlike synonyms, are opposite in meaning.*

E. **Solve the antonym puzzles below for the underlined words in the passage.**

Remember, you are looking for the underlined words that are opposites of the clue words.

	Antonym Clue Word	Puzzle Word from Passage
1.	lively	☐☐☐☐☐☐
2.	damages	☐☐☐☐☐☐☐☐
3.	rare	☐☐☐☐☐☐
4.	worthless	☐☐☐☐☐☐☐☐
5.	faster	☐☐☐☐☐☐
6.	hurts	☐☐☐☐☐
7.	unknown	☐☐☐☐☐☐☐
8.	health	☐☐☐☐☐☐
9.	future	☐☐☐☐☐☐
10.	poisonous	☐☐☐☐☐☐☐☐☐
11.	unsure	☐☐☐☐☐☐☐
12.	destroys	☐☐☐☐☐☐☐

PROGRESS TEST ①

Recalling Details

A. Place "T" for true or "F" for false in the box beside each statement.

1. There are various types of ghosts according to ghost specialists. .... ☐

2. Crisis Apparition ghosts appear to strangers only. .... ☐

3. Tape recording ghosts use audio equipment. .... ☐

4. Poltergeists are mischievous ghosts. .... ☐

5. Human beings can control whether or not their heart beats. .... ☐

6. The heart has five chambers. .... ☐

7. A child's heart would beat 80 to 100 times per minute. .... ☐

8. Christian Barnard was the first heart transplant recipient. .... ☐

9. The first heart transplant recipient died 19 days after the operation. .... ☐

10. Some butterflies use their colour as a camouflage. .... ☐

11. Most butterflies feed on nectar. .... ☐

12. There are three stages of the butterfly's life cycle. .... ☐

13. The earth's surface is made up of 7 large land masses. .... ☐

14. The water surface of the earth is divided into 6 oceans. .... ☐

15. Grid lines on a map that run east-west are called lines of longitude. .... ☐

16. Lines of longitude are called meridians. .... ☐

17. The equator divides the earth in halves. .... ☐

18. There are 60 minutes for each degree on an atlas. .... ☐

B. Circle the letters of the correct answers.

1. The Titanic was thought to be

   A. the fastest ship.   B. the largest ship.   C. unsinkable.

2. The Titanic left Southampton to go to

   A. Boston.   B. New York.   C. Montreal.

3. The number of people that died on the Titanic was

   A. over 1,500.   B. fewer than 1,000.   C. over 2,200.

4. The Lusitania transported passengers between

   A. England and France. B. England and Germany.   C. Ireland and America.

5. The Lusitania sank because

   A. it hit an iceberg.   B. it had a faulty engine.   C. it was torpedoed.

6. The Britannic was a luxury liner converted to a

   A. hospital ship.   B. cargo ship.   C. battleship.

7. The Britannic sank because

   A. it hit a rock.   B. it hit a mine or was torpedoed.   C. it was overloaded.

8. In the Renaissance period, women were not allowed to

   A. get married.   B. have children.   C. go to university.

9. In the 16th century, one could finish university without

   A. being able to write.   B. going to school.   C. speaking French.

10. In the Renaissance Period, scholars were interested in

    A. plant life.   B. science.   C. leisure.

11. A popular herbal medicine used today is

    A. tree bark.   B. rice.   C. ginseng.

12. Topical treatment refers to plants that help heal the

    A. outer body.   B. inner soul.   C. vital organs.

C. Underline the nouns and put parentheses ( ) around the verbs in the following sentences.

There may be more than one verb or noun in a sentence. Also, the noun does not have to be the subject.

1. She likes eating ice cream on a hot day.

2. He tripped over his shoelace and fell down the stairs.

3. The weather was fine.

4. The boys and girls played in the same yard.

5. Jim, John, and Sam walked to school together.

6. Linda is five years older than Susan.

7. The neighbours held a garage sale on their street.

8. Winter is a long and cold season.

9. Time is wasted when we do nothing.

10. The clock struck three and the school bell rang.

Subject and Predicate

The subject is the performer of the action of verb and its modifiers; the verb is the action in the sentence and its modifiers.

D. Match each subject with a suitable predicate.

1. Everyone

2. The old man

3. Bob and Billy

4. The Toronto Maple Leafs

5. The driver

6. Skiing

7. People in Nunavut

A relied on the use of his cane.

B had a good time at the party.

C practised in the old arena.

D prepare for a long and cold winter.

E can be dangerous if you fall.

F both made the swim team.

G could not stop in time.

Pronouns

A pronoun is used in place of a noun or to refer to a noun used previously in a sentence.

E. Fill in the blanks in the following sentences with pronouns.

1. The parents watched his/their _____ children playing.

2. He/She _____ likes to eat her lunch outdoors.

3. John told we/me _____ about his/their _____ problem.

4. They/We _____ bought themselves ice cream cones.

5. Susan asked when she/ her _____ would be allowed to go home.

Adjectives and Adverbs

Adjectives describe nouns while adverbs describe verbs.

F. Circle the adjectives and underline the adverbs in the sentences below.

1. The blazing sun sank slowly in the West.

2. The happy child opened her birthday present quickly.

3. Slowly but surely, the skilled skiers slipped down the hill.

4. Karen, a tall girl, was chosen immediately for the basketball team.

5. He ran swiftly between the stone obstacles on the sandy beach.

Direct and Indirect Objects

G. Underline the direct object and circle the indirect object in each sentence.

1. He gave me the ball.

2. She told Janet to come home.

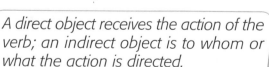

A direct object receives the action of the verb; an indirect object is to whom or what the action is directed.

3. The parents gave their son a new bicycle.

4. The quarterback threw the running back the ball for a touchdown.

5. The teacher gave us one more chance to finish our work.

H. Match the words from the passages with the definitions.

1.	ancient	A	unaware, no knowledge of
2.	transparent	B	the beginning of, starting point
3.	eerie	C	all the time, regularly
4.	oblivious	D	old, from years past
5.	chaos	E	expensive, tasteful, luxurious
6.	consistently	F	well-known, well-liked
7.	resume	G	under water
8.	elegant	H	left, went away
9.	departed	I	see-through
10.	submerged	J	scary, weird, haunted
11.	origin	K	disorder, mixed up, confusion
12.	popular	L	continue, carry on

Words Often Confused

I.   Choose the correct word for the meaning of each sentence.

1. She wrote in her dairy, diary _____ daily.

2. They're, There _____ going to arrive any minute now.

3. He came forth, fourth _____ in the race.

4. She accomplished an amazing feet, feat _____.

5. He couldn't decide weather, whether _____ or not to play.

6. The enemies fought a duel, dual _____.

7. He two, too, to _____ will enjoy the show.

8. He was sitting so far away he couldn't here, hear _____.

Forming New Words

J. Choose the proper prefix or suffix for each of the words below.

Making Opposites

1. real   `in, un`   = _____
2. sincere   `in, un`   = _____
3. direct   `in, de`   = _____
4. patient   `un, im`   = _____
5. belief   `dis, un`   = _____
6. known   `non, un`   = _____
7. proper   `un, im`   = _____
8. behave   `mis, dis`   = _____
9. certain   `dis, un`   = _____
10. believable   `un, im`   = _____

Other New Words

11. rely   `ness, able`   = _____
12. depend   `ive, able`   = _____
13. ride   `ing, ness`   = _____
14. happy   `able, ness`   = _____
15. cry   `able, ing`   = _____
16. appoint   `ive, ment`   = _____

Descriptive Language

K. Change the words in parentheses to the more descriptive words from below.

elderly   drenched   hilarious   bitterly   antique   kind   spacious   delicious   pelting

1. Dinner was (good) _____.

2. The movie was (very funny) _____.

3. The winter night was (very) _____ cold.

4. The (nice) _____ person helped the (old) _____ lady.

5. They were (wet) _____ from the (amount of) _____ rain.

6. The (big) _____ room was filled with (old) _____ furniture.

J.K. Rowling – Her Story

The success of the Harry Potter series of novels for adolescents is a modern day phenomenon. Millions of copies have been sold worldwide. When J.K. Rowling made a personal appearance in Toronto at the SkyDome, she drew the largest crowd ever recorded for a public reading session.

J.K. Rowling is now enjoying fame and wealth but it wasn't always that way. When she began to write the first Harry Potter book, she was a single mother of an infant daughter living on social assistance. She lived in a tiny rented apartment in Edinburgh, Scotland. She spent time in a local cafe where she wrote her first story, *Harry Potter and The Sorcerer's Stone*. This novel completely changed her life.

As a child, J.K. Rowling loved English Literature. She wrote her first real story at the age of 6. It was then that she decided that she wanted to become a writer. She thought writing would be the best occupation because she would be getting paid to do something she enjoyed.

J. K. Rowling isn't absolutely sure where she gets the ideas for the Harry Potter stories. The odd names for her characters come from a variety of sources. Some of her characters are loosely based on real people that she knows. However, once she starts to develop the characters, they become different from their source. The Potter stories are not based on Rowling's life, although most authors put a little of themselves into their writing.

Rowling's favourite author is Jane Austin. She also enjoys reading the humorous works of Roddy Doyle. Humour is an important ingredient in her writing. As a child, her favourite book was *The Little Horse* by Elizabeth Goudge. However, she isn't certain that she was directly influenced by anything she read in her youth.

Through the Harry Potter series, J.K. Rowling has been credited with increasing the interest in reading for children around the world.

The Main Idea

A. **Circle the letter of the most appropriate statement that gives the main idea of each paragraph.**

Paragraph One

A. Harry Potter is an interesting character.   B. J.K. Rowling is a popular author.
C. Harry Potter novels are interesting.   D. J.K. Rowling enjoys writing.

Paragraph Two

A. J.K. Rowling is wealthy.   B. J.K. Rowling was a poor author.
C. J.K. Rowling drinks coffee.   D. Harry Potter saved her life.

Paragraph Three

A. Six-year-olds can be writers.   B. Write when you're young.
C. J.K. Rowling loved literature.   D. Don't write unless you get paid.

Paragraph Four

A. J.K. Rowling writes about people that she knows.
B. The characters in her books are sometimes based on real people.
C. Her characters are all made up.
D. Her novels are based strictly on her life.

Paragraph Five

A. J.K. Rowling enjoys reading other authors' works.
B. Humour is not important in her works.
C. Rowling was influenced by reading as a child.
D. Jane Austin influenced her works.

Your Opinion

B. **Answer the question.**

Why is J.K. Rowling credited with changing the reading habits of children around the world?

_____

_____

Types of Sentences

- There are four main types of sentences:
  1. Declarative – simply makes a statement and ends with a period.

     Example: John caught the ball.

  2. Interrogative – asks a question and ends with a question mark.

     Example: What time is it?

  3. Imperative – gives a command or makes a request and ends with a period.

     Example: Answer the telephone.

  4. Exclamatory – expresses emotion or strong feelings and ends with an exclamation mark.

     Example: Help me, I'm falling!

C. Punctuate each of the following sentences and state the type of sentence in the space provided.

| Decl. Declarative | Int. Interrogative | Imp. Imperative | Excl. Exclamatory |

1. Look out

2. Stop before it's too late

3. I think it is time to leave

4. The sun is shining today

5. Where did I put my wallet

6. Where did he go after school

7. Wash your hands before dinner

8. Pick up those books on the floor

Don't forget to punctuate the sentences.

D. Compose your own sentences.

Declarative: _____

Interrogative: _____

Imperative: _____

Exclamatory: _____

Building Vocabulary

E. Change the word in parentheses in each sentence to a form that fits the sense of the sentence.

> Example: John (give) is _____ away his bicycle.
>
> You would place the word "giving" in the space, which is a form of the word "give" in parentheses.

1. Paul (ran) will _____ to the store before it closes.

2. Judy (call) _____ her friends last night.

3. The dog (growl) _____ at the mailman.

4. It was a (beauty) _____ morning with the sunshine.

5. He was very (help) _____ when he was needed.

6. Be (care) _____ when you go swimming.

7. Show (kind) _____ towards others.

8. The children stood in a perfect (form) _____.

9. She could not find the (solve) _____ to the problem.

10. It was (terrible) _____ cold outside.

11. They were studying the (move) _____ of the earth.

12. The wedding was followed by a (celebrate) _____.

Making Opposites

F. Add the proper prefixes to the words and write the opposites.

1.	un/im	_____ prepared	2.	dis/un	_____ appointed
3.	dis/un	_____ fair	4.	un/im	_____ proper
5.	im/un	_____ possible	6.	un/dis	_____ honour
7.	un/dis	_____ approve	8.	dis/un	_____ likely
9.	dis/un	_____ happy	10.	in/un	_____ complete
11.	dis/un	_____ necessary	12.	im/un	_____ perfect

Games and Toys of Pioneer Canada (1)

The toys children play with today are often highly technical and electronic, and involve the use of a computer. The children of pioneer Canada, however, did not have such advanced toys and games as these. Instead, they relied on making their own toys and creating interactive games that involved simple physical action.

Although their toys were simple, pioneer children were never bored. After a hard day's work helping their parents on the homestead, they looked forward to free time for play. Many of their favourite games are still played today. Blindman's buff and hide-and-seek are examples of old games that are still played today. A rope tied to a tree made a perfect swing and a plank over a saw-horse made an ideal seesaw. In playgrounds of today, the swing and the seesaw are still very popular. These playground favourites are perhaps better made today but are no more enjoyable than they were for pioneer children.

Nature provided not only the material for making toys but also the toy itself. A weeping willow tree beside a creek was an exciting toy. If a rope was not available, children would swing on a willow branch over the creek and let go, creating a splash. This activity was a perfect way to cool off on a hot summer day.

Horseshoe pitching was one of the most popular games all across Canada. A wooden peg in the ground and a couple of horseshoes were all

that was needed. It was not only a game for children. Adults took this game very seriously and competitions between neighbours and towns were common. It is still a favourite backyard game and no community picnic is complete without a horseshoe pitching competition.

Drawing Conclusions

· A Conclusion is an opinion reached after considering facts and details.

A. Draw conclusions for the following questions.

1. Why were pioneer children happy to have simple toys?

   _____

   _____

2. Why would swinging from a tree over a creek be so much fun for pioneer children?

   _____

   _____

3. What facts in the story suggest that pioneer children were always busy?

   _____

   _____

4. What would lead you to believe that horseshoe pitching was a very important pastime in pioneer days?

   _____

   _____

5. How can nature and the use of one's imagination result in creating fun and interesting games?

   _____

   _____

Recalling Facts

B. Explain how you would make the following toys. Be sure to mention all the materials you would need.

① a seesaw

② a swing

③ a horseshoe pit

Punctuation – Commas and Quotation Marks

- Place Quotation Marks ("...") around the exact words spoken by a person.

  Example: Paul said, "I am going home now."
  Note: a comma is placed after the word "said" but not before it.

  Example: He said, "Good morning." Note: a comma after "said".
  "Good morning," he said. Note: a comma after "morning".

- Place a Comma between words in a series.

  Example: I like to eat potatoes, tomatoes, carrots, and beans.

- Special Note: Place a capital at the beginning of a quotation.

C. Punctuate the following sentences where necessary.

1. She screamed Look out

2. Linda yelled Is anyone there

3. He played baseball soccer basketball and hockey

4. Let's go swimming said Janet to her friends

5. The teacher said tonight for homework you have Math Science and Spelling

Quotation marks are used to show people speaking. In composition, this is called dialogue. Another way of writing dialogue is to list the speakers, each followed by a colon, and their speech.
Example: John: How are you today, Paul?
          Paul: I'm fine, how are you?
Note: when you use this method, you do not need quotation marks.

D. Write a conversation between you and a friend. Place the speaker's name before the colon.

	: _____
	: _____
	: _____
	: _____

Poet's Corner

- When the 1st and 2nd lines rhyme, and the 3rd and 4th lines of a poem rhyme, the poem is following an "aa/bb" rhyming scheme. Lines of poetry placed together form a verse.

    Example: The morning sun shines <u>bright</u>
    Day replaces <u>night</u>
    Flowers awake from their <u>sleep</u>
    Birds sing cheep, <u>cheep</u>.

E. **Use this rhyming scheme (aa/bb) to compose either a two-verse poem or two one-verse poems.**

Here is an opportunity to become a poet. Use the rhyming words below or create your own to compose a simple poem. Here are some rhyming words to work with.

high/try/sigh/fly/sky/sly   long/song/strong   free/tree/see/sea/me

same/name/tame/came/fame   ate/plate   mouse/house   feed/need/seed

Your title: _____

_____

_____

_____

_____

Your title: _____

_____

_____

_____

_____

Games and Toys of Pioneer Canada (2)

Since there were no manufactured toys available to pioneer children, they had to be very creative when it came to making their own toys. A simple ball was made out of a stuffed pig's bladder, which was sturdy enough to be kicked around the field without breaking open. The name "pigskin" which referred to this type of ball is a term still in use today. Hoop rolling was also a popular game. An iron or wooden hoop and a stick were all that was needed. The challenge was to see who could keep it rolling the longest.

With Canadian winters being so cold, indoor games were important. The pioneer children did not have malls, movie theatres, or skating rinks for shelter from the winter weather. Shadow picture making was a family favourite. They would seat a family member in front of a candle and hold up a sheet of paper. A silhouette was created and then traced.

Many games were useful in helping boys and girls prepare for adult life. Girls made rag dolls and sewed clothing. These were not as perfect in form as today's Barbie but were enjoyed just as much, and valuable skills were learned. Boys went hunting and fishing with their fathers. Making a strong fishing rod out of a tree branch was an important skill. Aside from putting food on the table, fishing was a relaxing summer pastime for a pioneer boy. Boys were skilled with knives and learned the art of carving, which was useful for making toys for their younger brothers and sisters. A pocketknife could be used to make a sturdy bow and arrow set or wooden soldiers.

Pioneer life was not as fast-paced as life today. Without automobiles, travel was rare and much time was spent around the home. Therefore the pioneer children had to find things to do to occupy their time. Even though they were without television and radio, life was never dull. There was always work to do, fields and streams to play in, and the creative art of toy making to keep them busy.

Skimming

A. Re-read the passage very quickly, taking in as many facts as you can. Once you have finished that second reading, answer the factual questions below. Try to answer with the exact facts from the passage.

1.   What was a ball made from?   _____

2.   What was the name of this type of ball?   _____

3.   What game was played with a hoop and a stick? _____

4.   In the game of shadow making, what was traced? _____

5.   What toy did girls make?   _____

6.   What was used to make a fishing rod?   _____

7.   Why was travel rare in pioneer days?   _____

Fact or Opinion

•   *A Fact refers to information that is given exactly from the passage. An Opinion is your interpretation of the information in the passage.*

B. For each statement below, place "F" for fact or "O" for opinion in the space provided.

1. Pioneer children were never bored. .... ☐

2. Pioneer boys relaxed when they went fishing. .... ☐

3. Girls could be creative when making their dolls. .... ☐

4. A pocketknife could be used to make wooden soldiers. .... ☐

5. There were no manufactured toys available to pioneer children. .... ☐

Prepositions

- A Preposition helps connect a noun or pronoun to another part of the sentence. It also connects a verb to other words in the sentence.

  Example: The students in the class read quietly.

  The word "in" connects the subject, students, to the class. Now we know that they are the students from the class.

  Example: He placed his hat on the hook.

  The word "on" connects the verb "placed" to the word "hook", which is where the hat is placed.

C. **Choose eight prepositions from the list below and use each to create a sentence. After each sentence, place the letter "N" if the preposition connects a noun to other words, and a "V" if it connects the verb to other words.**

after   down   into   under   inside   near   without   until   beside   at
above   around   below   of   on   for   from   before   among   about   with

1. The children played baseball in the yard. | V |

2. _____ | |

3. _____ | |

4. _____ | |

5. _____ | |

6. _____ | |

7. _____ | |

8. _____ | |

9. _____ | |

Word Games

- *Anagrams – An Anagram is a word in which the letters can be moved around to form another word.*

  Example: *The letters in "tries" can be rearranged to make "tires".*

D. Make new words using the clues. Do not add letters.

rats	look up to the sky	1.
ocean	boat that is easy to tip	2.
stop	cooking utensils	3.
cheap	soft fruit	4.
could	holds the rain	5.

Homophones

- *Homophones are words that sound the same but are spelled differently and have different meanings.*

E. Fill in the crossword blanks with homophones.

1. clothing

   w h [e] r e

2. ears

   h [e] r e

3. tossed

   t h [r] o u g h

4. horse's ____

   m [a] i n

5. no strength

   w [e] e k

6. wind

   s [a] l e

Medieval Castles

Medieval castles were built to house the local lords and their families. Inhabitants of the castles usually had their own apartments. Castles were equipped with a nursery, a brewhouse, a school, a chapel, a library, many bedrooms, and an elegant dining room. The dining room was furnished with a grand table for entertaining important guests. Fireplaces were numerous throughout a castle and provided the main source of heat for the apartments. Bedrooms had huge four-poster beds with soft feather pillows and thick curtains to prevent drafts.

The main purpose of a castle was protection. A lord who owned a large amount of land would lease the land out to farmers who would pay him farm produce as rent. He would offer protection against enemy attacks. In the case of an attack, villagers would gather within the castle walls and help defend the castle against invaders. As a result, villages were established near the castle.

Castles were expensive to run. It would cost millions of dollars by today's standards to build and maintain a castle. A noble in medieval times would have an income of about £1,000 or $2,500 per year. An ordinary working person might earn the equivalent of one dollar a year. But castle owners had huge expenses. They often employed 300 people to perform various tasks.

In the late 1500's, when battles became large-scale events, castles were not needed. Today, many castles in Europe have been converted into hotels and guesthouses. Many castles are for sale by owners who cannot afford to occupy them. In fact, castles can be purchased for a lot less than you would expect. The real cost comes once you move in and try to pay for the household expenses.

Finding Supporting Facts

A. For each case, place a check mark beside the information that best proves the statement given.

1. Medieval castles were not built for local people.

    A. ☐ Castles were too far from the village.

    B. ☐ Castles were occupied by lords and ladies.

    C. ☐ Local people did not like castles.

2. Castles were well equipped.

    A. ☐ There were high walls around the castle.

    B. ☐ A castle had a library, ballroom, nursery, and a school.

    C. ☐ Castles were used for defence against invaders.

3. The castle was used for protection.

    A. ☐ Villagers hid inside the castle when being attacked.

    B. ☐ Only the lord of the castle was protected.

    C. ☐ The castle was evacuated during an attack.

4. It cost a great deal of money to run a castle.

    A. ☐ Some castles employed 300 people.

    B. ☐ Castles needed many repairs.

    C. ☐ Castle furniture was expensive.

5. Noblemen were wealthy in medieval times.

    A. ☐ Nobles worked very hard to earn money.

    B. ☐ Local farmers paid heavy taxes.

    C. ☐ A nobleman could have an income of £1,000 a year.

6. Fewer castles were being built.

    A. ☐ There were not enough building materials.

    B. ☐ There were no workers to build the castles.

    C. ☐ Battles were large-scale events and fought on battlefields.

Prepositions and Objects

- A Preposition is often followed by a noun acting as object of the preposition.
  Example: He climbed over the fence.
  The preposition is "over" and "fence" is the noun, object of the preposition.

B.   Underline the object of the preposition in each of the following sentences.

1.   The clouds flew across the sky.

2.   In the morning, she went jogging.

3.   They ate lunch beside the pond.

4.   Within the school, there are many different students.

5.   After the rain, the road was slippery.

C.   Finish each rhyme by adding the appropriate noun as object of the preposition.

Do you remember the nursery rhymes you enjoyed when you were little?

1.   The cow jumped over the _____ .

2.   Little Miss Muffet sat on her _____ .

3.   Jack and Jill went up the _____ .

4.   Humpty Dumpty sat on a _____ .

5.   Hickory Dickory Dock the mouse ran up the _____ .

D.   Create sentences, adding prepositions and objects where necessary.

1.   _____ around the block.

2.   _____ beneath the ground.

3.   After the game, _____ .

4.   _____ into the closet.

5.   Before school began, _____ .

6.   _____ between the houses.

Plural Forms

E. **Circle the proper plural forms and complete the rules of spelling in your own words.**

1. knife – knifes / knives	2. life – lives / lifes
3. half – halves / halfs	
Rule: For some words ending in "f" or "fe", change _____ .	
4. army – armies / armys	5. diary – diarys / diaries
6. city – citys / cities	7. lady – ladys / ladies
Rule: For words ending in "y" with a consonant (e.g. m, r, t, d) before the "y", drop _____ .	
8. journey– journies / journeys	9. key – keys / keies
10. valley – valleies / valleys	
Rule: For some words ending in "y" with a vowel (e.g. e) before the "y", add _____ .	

Challenge

F. **Form the plurals of the following words.**

1. goose _____   2. child _____   3. foot _____

4. man _____   5. tooth _____   6. mouse _____

7. What do these words have in common in terms of their plural forms?

sheep   aircraft   deer   moose   grass   salmon

_____

The Thinking Organ

Of all the <u>organs</u> in the human body, none is more <u>vital</u> than the brain. The brain is what gives us our identity. The acts of making decisions, solving problems, and identifying objects are all the direct responsibility of the brain.

The human brain stops growing when we are about six or seven years of age. When its growth is complete, the brain weighs about 3 kilograms. The brain is the most <u>amazing</u> and <u>complex</u> object we know. It takes care of the <u>creative</u> things we do such as painting pictures, writing stories, designing buildings, or building computers. The brain processes information from all around us. When a traffic light turns red, we know not to cross the street or when a dog growls at us, we know to keep away. Much of this information is <u>stored</u> in our memory. The brain also controls all our <u>emotions</u>.

The largest part of the brain is called the *cerebrum*, which controls the muscles and processes sight, sound, tastes, and smell messages. The left side of the cerebrum controls the right side of the body and the right side controls the left side of the body. The left side is <u>dominant</u>, which accounts for why most people are right-handed. Below the cerebrum is the *cerebellum* that controls balance and co-ordination. Near the cerebellum is the *medulla oblongata* that controls bodily functions such as breathing, swallowing, and vomiting. The *hypothalamus* controls our emotions, particularly anger and <u>fear</u>, and it controls body temperature, hunger, and thirst. The brain is also directly <u>connected</u> to our central nervous system.

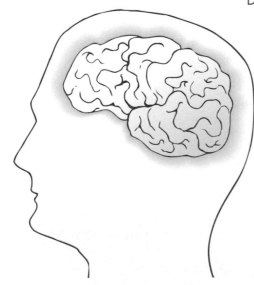

The brain has always been a <u>mystery</u> to mankind. We only know the basics of how it works. The more we study the brain and its <u>function</u>, the more we realize how complicated it is.

Recalling Details

A. Fill in the blanks in the passage below with the appropriate words.

| cerebellum | nervous | left | cerebrum | organ |
| hypothalamus | growing | process | memory | emotions |

The human brain is the most important 1._____ in the body. When we reach the age of six, the brain stops 2._____ . The main function of the brain is to 3._____ information. Much of this information is stored in our 4._____ . The brain also controls our 5._____ such as happiness and sadness. The 6._____ is the biggest part of the brain. It is above the 7._____ . Most people are right-handed because the 8._____ side of the brain is dominant. The 9._____ controls emotions and body temperature. The brain is connected to our central 10._____ system.

B. Match the facts from the passage with the descriptions or definitions.

1.	3 kilograms		A	controls hunger and thirst
2.	cerebrum		B	controls right side of body
3.	left side of brain		C	controls balance and co-ordination
4.	cerebellum		D	largest part of the brain
5.	medulla oblongata		E	weight of the brain
6.	hypothalamus		F	controls bodily functions

Your Opinion

C. Why do you think that the brain is still a mystery to scientists today?

_____

_____

Conjunctions

- Conjunctions are words that join words, clauses, and phrases in a sentence.

  Example 1 *Conjunctions join nouns:*
  Caitlin or Kara will take her to school.

  Example 2 *Conjunctions join verbs:*
  He ran and jumped.

  Example 3 *Conjunctions join clauses:*
  It was a warm day although the sky was cloudy.

  Example 4 *Conjunctions join two sentences into one:*
  Paul walked home. He met a friend. → *Paul walked home and met a friend.*

D. Complete the sentences below with appropriate conjunctions.

and	or	but	if	since
because	while	until	so	unless

1. Peter _____ Roger were on the same team.

2. She won't wear it _____ it fits properly.

3. He has been tired ever _____ he caught a cold.

4. She was happy _____ it was her birthday.

5. Either Sheila _____ Martha will say the speech.

6. He waited in the car _____ she went shopping.

7. He made the decision _____ it was not popular.

8. She will help you _____ you help yourself.

9. They made the rules _____ it was their responsibility.

10. She couldn't wait _____ the holidays came.

Use each conjunction in the list above once only.

New Words – Synonyms and Antonyms

- A Synonym is a word that means the same as a select word and an Antonym is a word that has an opposite meaning of a select word.

E. **Use the underlined words in the reading passage to complete the following word puzzles.**

1.	simple (antonym)	o		l	
2.	main (synonym)		m		a	
3.	boring (antonym)		a		n	
4.	body parts (synonym)		g	
5.	solution (antonym)			t		r	
6.	feelings (synonym)	m		i	
7.	linked (synonym)			e		e	
8.	courage (antonym)	e	
9.	unimportant (antonym)		t	
10.	imaginative (synonym)		c		t		v	
11.	use (synonym)	u		t		o	
12.	saved (synonym)		o		e	

F. **Use two of the words from the puzzles above in each of the two sentences of your own.**

1. _____

_____

2. _____

_____

Try to be creative.

The Origins of Money

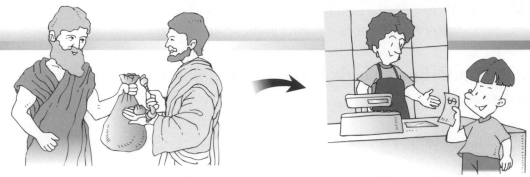

When we want to make a purchase today, we use money. We have many options as to how we pay with money. We can use a credit card, a debit card, a personal cheque, or cash. There is a price attached to the merchandise to show how much it is worth.

In ancient times, when money was non-existent, people bartered (traded) goods and services for other goods and services that they needed. Items such as shells, beads, metal, gold, jewelry, feathers, and tools were always welcome in a trade. Instead of simply trading goods and services, a crude form of currency was established by tribes around the world.

In Africa and Asia, shells were used as currency while in North America, the Indians used necklaces and headdresses in place of money. In Central Africa, copper rods called congas were used as currency. For ten of these rods, a native could buy himself a wife. In China, bronze miniatures were used to purchase the actual articles they represented. For example, a tiny replica of a tool would be used to purchase that exact tool. Probably the most popular form of currency was the use of animals. Cattle, pigs, and camels are still used today to purchase products or make payments by some tribes in Asia.

With the growth of cities, standard forms of payment became necessary to regulate the value of goods. The barter method worked nicely between individuals or in a village setting, but it lacked consistency. There was no standard by which a person could measure the value of what they were buying. It was difficult to be sure that the deal was fair. Often the one who was the shrewdest dealer profited the most. It was necessary to establish a regular system. This marked the beginning of money as we know it today.

Remembering Facts & Making Assumptions

A. Answer the following questions based on the reading passage.

1. Name four methods of payment we can use today.

   a. _____   b. _____

   c. _____   d. _____

2. What does bartering mean?

   _____

3. Make a list of things that were used as currency in ancient times.

   a. _____   b. _____

   c. _____   d. _____

4. Why was the use of bronze miniatures a clever way to make a purchase?

   _____

   _____

5. Why do you think that animals were such a popular form of currency?

   _____

   _____

6. Why was the bartering system not always fair?

   _____

   _____

Your Opinion

B. What skills would you need to possess to make you good at bartering? Can you describe your three choices?

1. _____

2. _____

3. _____

Adjective and Adverb Phrases

- Recall: An Adjective describes a noun.
  An Adverb describes a verb.
  A Phrase is a group of words that tells what a noun is like or where, when, or how the action of a verb takes place.
  Phrases begin with prepositions.

  Example 1   The boys in the class sat at the back.
  In this sentence, there is both an adjective phrase (in the class) and an adverb phrase (at the back).

  Example 2   The gift in the box was made in Italy.
  The adjective phrase "in the box" describes the noun; the adverb phrase "in Italy" tells where the gift was made.

C. Underline the adjective phrase in each sentence and place parentheses ( ) around the adverb phrases.

1. The dog in the kennel barked loudly.

2. The teacher of grade four sat in his desk.

3. In the morning, the sun rose over the cliffs.

4. She hid under the desk.

5. He ran up the road and down the hill.

6. Under the rainbow, you will find a pot of gold.

Look for the prepositions first.

 Challenge

D. Create sentences with adjective or adverb phrases. Use the preposition given before each sentence space.

1.   (over)   _____ .

2. (beneath)   _____ .

3. (behind)   _____ .

4.   (of)   _____ .

5.   (in)   _____ .

6. (across)   _____ .

Haiku Poetry

- Haiku Poetry is a non-rhyming Japanese poem popular in the 19th century. It often dealt with nature as a theme.

- Haiku poetry consists of three lines with 5, 7, and 5 syllables in each line in that order.

  Example: Sun / surf / sand / and / sea   5 syllables

  Sail / boats / drift / ing / by / the /shore   7 syllables

  South / sea / wind / blow / ing   5 syllables

  The syllable breaks have been marked in the above poem. Notice that the poem is a collection of images (word pictures).

- Alliteration: Alliteration occurs when consecutive words begin with the same letter. In the poem above, there is sun, surf, sand, sea – all of which begin with the letter "s". Alliteration gives a poem a smooth rhythm and helps connect descriptive words and images.

E.   Compose two Haiku poems. You may choose from one of the following topics or create your own. Try to avoid using words that are not descriptive.

Topics:

Winter Night	Birds in Flight	The Storm
Summer Morning	The Lion's Den	Children Playing

Title: _____

_____

_____

_____

Title: _____

_____

_____

_____

New France – The Beginning Of Canada (1)

The interest in reaching the Far East through a northern passage was very high in Europe. The Spanish had established a foothold in South America and Mexico. The French and English, always rivals, were competing to discover a northern passage that would lead to China.

Francis I, king of France, selected Jacques Cartier to lead a voyage on a similar route to that taken by John Cabot in 1497. Cartier left France in 1534 with 2 ships and 60 men. In less than three weeks, he had crossed the Atlantic and reached Newfoundland. He explored the surrounding area known today as Prince Edward Island and New Brunswick. He erected a flag on Gaspé Peninsula and claimed the land for France. Cartier convinced an Indian chief named Donnaconna to allow him to take his two sons back to France. Cartier wanted to impress the king.

When he returned to France, Cartier was considered a hero. The king was so pleased with his efforts that he allowed for a second voyage. In 1535, Cartier set sail again with 3 ships and 110 men. When they reached the Gulf of St. Lawrence, the Indians returning with him led Cartier to the St. Lawrence River. Impressed by the size of the river, Cartier thought that the St. Lawrence River might lead to a passage to the East.

Continuing west down the St. Lawrence River, Cartier reached what is today Montreal. He named the village Mount Réal (Royal Mountain) in honour of the height of the mountain in the village. This was as far as Cartier could go because a short distance up the river, he came across rapids that were impassable. Cartier was forced to spend the winter there. He and his men were not prepared for the Canadian winter. They suffered severe cold, a shortage of food and supplies, and the onset of scurvy.

Examining Facts – True or False

A. Place "T" for true and "F" for false beside each statement in the space provided.

1. Europeans wanted a northern route to the East. .... ☐

2. The Spanish had settlements in South America. .... ☐

3. Cartier's route was different from Cabot's. .... ☐

4. Francis I was king of France in 1534. .... ☐

5. Cartier made it to Newfoundland in less than three weeks. .... ☐

6. Cartier explored the area around P.E.I. and New Brunswick. .... ☐

7. On his first voyage, Cartier left France with 200 men. .... ☐

8. Cartier brought Indians back to France to impress the king. .... ☐

9. Cartier took the sons of Donnaconna back to France. .... ☐

10. Cartier was not interested in the St. Lawrence River. .... ☐

11. Cartier visited a village which today is Montreal. .... ☐

12. Cartier's voyage was stopped because of rapids. .... ☐

There are 3 false statements.

B. Compare facts about Cartier's two voyages in the chart below.

		1st Voyage	2nd Voyage
1.	Date		
2.	Number of Ships and Men in the Crew		
3.	Important Accomplishments		

Rules of Capitalization

- Here are some rules to remember:
  1. Use capitals at the beginning of sentences and questions.
  2. Use capitals for all proper names and titles.
  3. Use capitals for book and poem titles.
  4. Use capitals for months of the year and special days.
  5. Use capitals for brand names, company names, and religious terms.
  6. Use capitals for names of countries, cities, lakes, rivers, and regions.

C. In the following passage, there are numerous words that should be capitalized. Change the small letters to capitals where necessary.

in the month of june, professor smith took his wife mary and his children, jake, mark, and jordan, on a fishing trip up to moon river in the muskoka area of northern ontario. the drive from toronto took three hours but they stopped for lunch at mcdonald's. because the drive was so long, jordan brought his book entitled the best way to catch fish. he thought this book might help him learn how to fish. he was going to use the special fish hook called a surehook that he received for a birthday gift in may. it was made by the acme fishing gear company located in montreal. when they arrived, they passed the old st. luke's church down the road from the river. working outside the church was pastor rodgers, who also likes to fish. he waved at them as they went by.

In fact, there are 43 capitals missing. Can you find them?

New Words in Context - Crossword Puzzles

- *We can determine the meaning of a word by the idea behind the sentence in which it appears.*

D. Solve the crossword puzzles for the underlined words in the passage.

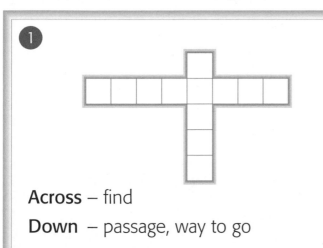

1

Across – find
Down – passage, way to go

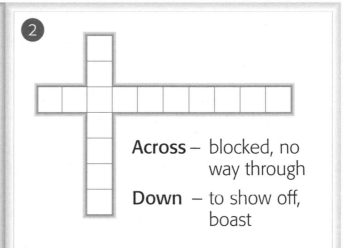

2

Across – blocked, no way through
Down – to show off, boast

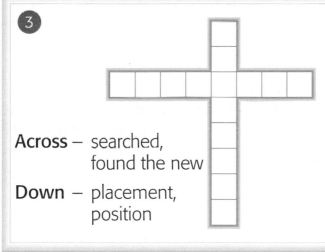

3

Across – searched, found the new
Down – placement, position

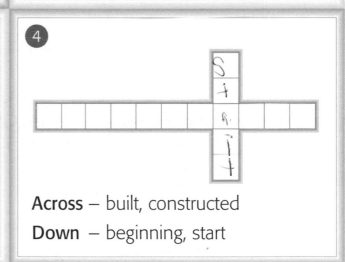

4

Across – built, constructed
Down – beginning, start

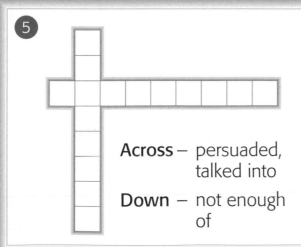

5

Across – persuaded, talked into
Down – not enough of

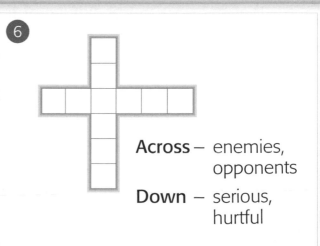

6

Across – enemies, opponents
Down – serious, hurtful

New France – The Beginning Of Canada (2)

After the <u>miserable</u> winter of 1535, twenty-five of Cartier's men had died. With the surviving crew, Cartier <u>prepared</u> to leave in the spring. He was returning to France with a new plan in mind. In addition to the search for the passage to the Orient, Cartier wanted to convince the king of France to support him in the search for the rich kingdom of the Saguenay. He kidnapped Donnaconna, the Indian chief, to use as evidence to the king that this wealthy kingdom existed.

When Cartier returned, France was at war with Spain. Although the king of France agreed to finance a third voyage, Cartier would have to wait. In 1541, he finally set sail again with five ships and a thousand <u>settlers</u>.

Cartier established a settlement at present day Quebec City. From there, he tried to find the kingdom of the Saguenay. He was doomed to <u>failure</u> because no kingdom existed. Once again a harsh winter brought <u>hardship</u> and illness. Worse still, Cartier was <u>attacked</u> by natives. In the spring, Cartier abandoned the settlement. He brought back quartz and iron pyrites, minerals that he <u>thought</u> were valuable. Also known as "fool's gold", these minerals were worthless.

Cartier's explorations were failures but the impact on Canadian history is significant. In 1608, Champlain established a settlement in Quebec City that became the beginning of the <u>development</u> of Canada as a nation. Settlements sprang up along the St. Lawrence and by the middle of the 17th century, New France was firmly established.

The English and the French <u>fought</u> over this territory. At the historic battle on the Plains of Abraham in Quebec City, the English, under General Wolfe, defeated Montcalm and the French. However, the French maintained their language, religion, and culture. Today, they continue in the struggle to protect these and keep the province of Quebec a French-speaking society.

Fact or Opinion

- A Fact is an exact statement given in the story. An Opinion is your personal point of view based on what you have read.

A. Place "F" for fact and "O" for opinion for each statement in the space provided.

1. Canadian winters can be harsh. .... ☐

2. It is easier to travel in the spring. .... ☐

3. 25 of Cartier's men died. .... ☐

4. Cartier thought there were riches in the Saguenay. .... ☐

5. Cartier was cruel to Donnaconna. .... ☐

6. Cartier wanted to prove to the king that there were riches in the Saguenay region. .... ☐

7. France and Spain did not get along. .... ☐

8. Cartier was anxious to build a settlement. .... ☐

9. There were no riches in the Saguenay region. .... ☐

10. Quartz and iron pyrites could be used as jewelry. .... ☐

B. In your opinion, was Cartier a success or a failure? Make a list of his successes and his failures in the chart below.

Accomplishments	Failures/Hardships
1.	1.
2.	2.
3.	3.

C. What natural wealth was there in Canada that Cartier overlooked?

_____

_____

_____

Problem Sentences

- *Sentence Fragments — a sentence fragment is an incomplete sentence.*

  Example: *When I walk home from school...*
  This fragment needs more information for it to make sense.

  If you add "I see my friends on the way", then you would have:
  When I walk home from school, I see my friends on the way.

D. Correct the following sentence fragments by adding the necessary information.

1.   During my lunch hour, _____ .

2.   After it stopped raining, _____ .

3.   _____ because the teacher asked.

4.   If it isn't too late, _____ .

5.   While I am watching television, _____ .

Combining Sentences

- *Some sentences are too short. They are better when combined with another sentence that refers to the same topic.*

  Example: *It was Saturday morning. I woke up late.*
  Could become: It was Saturday morning and I woke up late. or
  This Saturday morning, I woke up late.

E.   Combine the following short sentences.

Don't forget to use conjunctions.

1.   Carol called on Julie. Julie was not home.

_____

2.   Friday is a holiday. There is no school.

_____

3.   My teacher is very nice. Mrs. Smith is my teacher. She teaches grade four.

_____

4.   Phillip had a doctor's appointment. It was on Tuesday.

_____

Word Builder Crossword Puzzles

F. Each puzzle contains three root words for the underlined words in the reading passage. Use the clues to help you solve the puzzles.

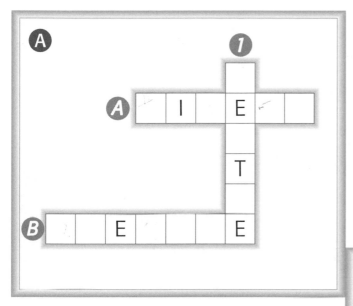

Crossword A

Across – A. sadness
B. get ready

Down – 1. make ready, calm, rest

Crossword B

Across – A. form an idea
B. build, make, form

Down – 1. firm, tough, difficult

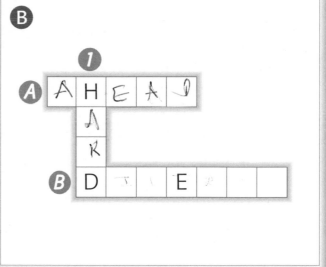

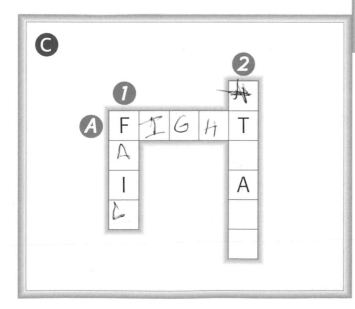

Crossword C

Across – A. battle

Down – 1. not win
2. charge

Multiple Choice

A. Circle the correct answer for each of the statements from the reading passages.

1. The number of Harry Potter books sold is
   A. thousands.   B. millions.   C. hundreds.

2. Before writing her books, J.K. Rowling was
   A. very wealthy.   B. a struggling single mother.
   C. a housewife.

3. Pioneer children got their toys from
   A. making their own.   B. hardware stores.   C. trading posts.

4. Many games and toys came from
   A. toy manufacturers.   B. the farm.
   C. nature and their surroundings.

5. The most popular games of pioneer times across Canada was
   A. hockey.   B. horseshoes.   C. lacrosse.

6. In pioneer times, a ball made from a pig's bladder was called
   A. a pigskin.   B. a pig ball.   C. a football.

7. A favourite father-son pastime in pioneer times was
   A. cooking.   B. sewing.   C. fishing.

8. When pioneer children weren't playing, they were
   A. doing chores.   B. sleeping.   C. watching television.

9. Early castles were not very comfortable because they were
   A. high on a hill.   B. too large.   C. cold and drafty.

10. The main purpose of a castle was
    A. to hold big parties.   B. to show wealth.   C. for protection.

11. The brain is the most important organ in the body because
   A. it is large.　　　　　　B. links to the nervous system.
   C. it helps us think.

12. The human brain stops growing when we are about
   A. 6 years old.　　　　B. 18 years old.　　　　C. 35 years old.

13. The human brain, when it is fully developed, weighs about
   A. 10 kg.　　　　　　B. 25 kg.　　　　　　C. 3 kg.

14. Before the use of money, deals were made by
   A. guessing.　　　　　B. bartering.　　　　　C. arguing.

15. For trade in China, people used
   A. bronze miniatures.　　B. snakeskin.　　　　C. furs.

16. The Spanish had made settlements in
   A. Australia.　　　　　B. New France.　　　　C. South America.

17. Cartier returned to France with
   A. riches.　　　　　　B. gold and jewels.　　C. an Indian chief.

18. Cartier's first two voyages were in
   A. 1492 and 1497.　　B. 1534 and 1535.　　C. 1620 and 1622.

19. Cartier thought that riches lay in
   A. the Saguenay Region.　B. the St. Lawrence River.　C. Montreal.

20. Cartier's men suffered from a disease called
   A. influenza.　　　　　B. scurvy.　　　　　　C. smallpox.

21. Cartier attempted to build a settlement at present day
   A. Toronto.　　　　　　B. Montreal.　　　　　C. Quebec City.

22. In 1608, a settlement in Quebec was established by
   A. King Francis I.　　　B. John Cabot.　　　　C. Champlain.

B. State whether the following sentences are declarative, imperative, interrogative, or exclamatory and punctuate them accordingly.

1. Get up, you're going to be late

2. Who will help with the work

3. Wow

4. This is the main street in town

C. Place commas where needed in the following sentences.

1. When the storm ended we came out to play.

2. I played basketball hockey football and tennis.

3. She said to the new student "Take any seat you like."

4. Peaches plums pears and nectarines are expensive in winter.

5. He shouted "Let me in it's cold outside!"

Prepositions and Phrases

D. Add a suitable preposition in the space provided.

1. He hid _____ the table.   under, through, inside

2. She sunbathed _____ the backyard.   under, into, in

3. The dog ran _____ the yard.   around, into, throughout

4. The students _____ grade four went on a field trip.   in, to, about

5. The boat sailed _____ the river.   into, down, between

E. Underline the prepositional phrase(s) in each sentence.

1. Under the rug, there was a lot of dirt.

2. They jumped into the pool.

3. The students in the local school helped at the fundraising.

4. In the morning, she went to her friend in the other part of town.

Conjunctions

Conjunctions join other words, phrases, or main ideas in a sentence.

F. Underline the conjunctions in the following sentences.

1. Decide whether you will stay or you will go.

2. Either Joe or Paul will be captain of the team.

3. It was warm although the forecast was for sunny weather.

4. It may taste bad but it's good for you.

5. She will not be late if she leaves on time.

A phrase is a group of words introduced by a preposition that describes either an adverb or a noun.

Adverb and Adjective Phrases

G. State whether the underlined words represent an adverb or an adjective phrase. Place ADV or ADJ in the space.

1. Go into the garage and get the lawnmower.

2. The players on the junior team practise every day.

3. The girls in the class sat in the front.

4. In the evening, they watched a movie.

5. The seat in the front cost much more money.

Capitalization

H. Correct the missing capitals in each sentence.

1. mr. smith asked john to meet him at lions stadium.

2. she said, "could someone please assist me?"

3. lauren and kara read a judy blume story.

4. he worked at the ministry of transport in downtown montreal.

5. they rented a cottage on rice lake in the kawartha region.

I. Match the words from the passages with the definitions.

1.	organs		A	searched, looked into
2.	vital		B	imaginative
3.	responsibility		C	serious, dangerous
4.	amazing		D	beginning, the start
5.	complex		E	unknown
6.	creative		F	enemies
7.	design		G	body parts
8.	stored		H	important
9.	dominant		I	duty
10.	mystery		J	not enough
11.	rivals		K	complicated, numerous
12.	explored		L	shape, figure, drawing
13.	severe		M	put away
14.	shortage		N	in charge, main, most important
15.	onset		O	surprising, unbelievable

J. Change the words to suit the sentences and agreement with verbs or subjects.

1. Yesterday Paul laugh _____ when he heard the joke.

2. The sun shone on the beauty _____ flowers.

3. The bird was chirp _____ loudly.

4. Crossing the road can be danger _____ .

5. She was perform _____ in the school play.

6. They lived happy _____ ever after.

7. He made a donate _____ to the charity.

8. Being on time proved that she was rely _____ .

9. The carpenter make _____ a cabinet.

10. The puppy was very life _____ .

11. The children were terrify _____ by the scary movie.

Plurals

K. Write the proper plural forms of the following words.

1.	hero		2.	army	
3.	city		4.	lady	
5.	life		6.	leaf	
7.	half		8.	tomato	
9.	potato		10.	mouse	

Building New Words from Root Words

L. Add a prefix or suffix to each of the words to make a new word.

1.	arrange		2.	organize	
3.	view		4.	connect	
5.	mind		6.	appoint	
7.	satisfied		8.	create	
9.	belief		10.	care	

Grammar

1 Nouns

A **Noun** is a word that represents a person, place, or thing. Nouns can be either Common or Proper.

Examples: Bicycle, dog, house, gymnasium, father, and child are all **Common Nouns**. They refer to **non-specific** persons, places, or things, and often represent a group or a classification.

Exercise A

In each group of words below, circle the one that is <u>not</u> a common noun.

1. book   jumps   window   cake
2. bulky   height   weight   size
3. television   camera   sings   performance
4. baseball   team   exciting   coach
5. tools   hammer   useful   nail
6. children   happy   school   classroom

Proper Nouns refer to **specific** persons, places, or things, and require capitalization.

Examples: Ford Explorer, Glen Road Public School, and Terry Fox are all **Proper Nouns** because they refer to **specific** persons, places, or things. Notice that these nouns begin with capital letters.

Exercise B

Identify the proper noun in each group below and capitalize its first letter.

1. harry potter   author   story   character
2. player   teammate   joe sakic   winger
3. opera   theatre   cn tower   stadium
4. bank   royal bank   teller   money
5. arena   air canada centre   rink   ice
6. amusement park   wonderland   circus   clowns

Exercise C

Underline both the common and proper nouns in the following sentences. Capitalize the proper nouns.

Do not include pronouns in your selections.

1. ramon gonzales and his sister, julia, attend williamson road public school.

2. They enjoy playing sports at recess time.

3. ramon is a very good basketball player while julia prefers to play volleyball.

4. The gonzales family moved to canada from spain three years ago and live in a downtown neighbourhood.

5. julia and ramon speak both spanish and english and are learning french in school.

6. mr. gonzales works as a computer programmer and mrs. gonzales is an interior decorator.

7. In the gonzales family there are four children, but only two of the children attend school.

8. Next summer, the family will visit their cousins in spain.

Noun Plurals

Here are five basic rules for making nouns plural; however, there are many exceptions to these rules.

Rule 1:   Most nouns form the plural by simply adding **s** to the singular nouns.
Examples: car – cars   bicycle – bicycles   boy – boys   girl – girls

Rule 2:   Nouns ending in **f** or **fe**
In some cases add **s** to the original nouns.
Examples: chief – chiefs   giraffe – giraffes

For most nouns ending in **f** or **fe**, change the **f** to **v** and add **es**.
Examples: life – lives   wife – wives

Rule 3:   Nouns ending in **s** or **sh**, **ch**, **x**, and **z**
Add **es** to the singular noun (if proper pronunciation requires the extra syllable).
Examples: wax – waxes   business – businesses

Rule 4:   a. If a consonant comes before the **y**, change the **y** to **i** and add **es**.
b. If a vowel comes before the **y**, then simply add **s**.
Examples: army – armies   city – cities   but   key – keys and valley – valleys

Rule 5:   a. If a vowel comes before the **o** ending, in most cases add **s**.
b. If a consonant comes before the **o** ending, in most cases add **es**.
Examples: rodeo – rodeos   but   hero – heroes

Exercise D

Change the following nouns to plural form. Check the rules above if you are not sure of the proper ending. Enter the Rule # that fits each change.

1. army   _____ Rule # ____   2. lunch   _____ Rule # ____

3. pen   _____ Rule # ____   4. duty   _____ Rule # ____

5. proof   _____ Rule # ____   6. lady   _____ Rule # ____

7. life   _____ Rule # ____   8. journey   _____ Rule # ____

9. half   _____ Rule # ____   10. patio   _____ Rule # ____

11. tax   _____ Rule # ____   12. radio   _____ Rule # ____

13. car   _____ Rule # ____   14. diary   _____ Rule # ____

15. church _____ Rule # ____   16. leaf   _____ Rule # ____

CHALLENGE

1. What do these nouns have in common?

   sheep   deer   moose   salmon   grass   aircraft

   Answer: _____

2. Write the plural form of the nouns below. They change completely and do not follow any rules.

   A. ox _____

   B. mouse _____

   C. child _____

   D. tooth _____

Collective Nouns are singular but refer to groups of people or things.

Example: "Orchestra" is a singular noun but refers to a number of musicians.

Exercise E

Complete the Collective Noun Crossword Puzzle.

Down

A. workers on a boat
B. all the players together
C. a group or a club
D. a group of soldiers
E. soldiers on the sea

Across

1. a country
2. a business
3. people gathering together

Crossword puzzle:

Down B: t e a (m)
Down D: a r m y
Down E: n a v y

Across 1: n a t i o n
Across 2: c o m p a n y
Across 3: c . w

Down A/C column: c r e w / p a n

2 Pronouns

A **Pronoun** is used in place of a noun. It refers to a person, place, or thing without naming it. It must agree in gender (male or female) and number (singular or plural) with the noun it is replacing.

Personal Pronouns

Singular: I   you   he   she   it   one   me   him   her
Plural: we   you   they   ones   us   them
Possessive: my   mine   our   ours   your   yours   his   her   hers   its   one's   their   theirs

Note: The noun that is being replaced by the pronoun is called its **Antecedent**.

Exercise A

Fill in each blank with the proper pronoun. Choose pronouns from the ones listed above.

> Make sure your choice of pronoun agrees with the verb, the antecedent noun in the sentences, or the other pronoun being used.

1. Paul's bicycle broke down so _____ needed repair.

2. The students brought _____ pets to school.

3. Shakira invited all the students to _____ birthday party.

4. The teacher asked _____ to show our homework.

5. At lunchtime the students often shared _____ treats.

6. Recess was a time for _____ to play our favourite games.

7. Our favourite game in the spring was baseball because _____ could be played with many participants.

8. _____ chose our teams for the baseball game by a random draw.

9. He asked _____ a question that I could not answer.

10. When the teacher asked who owned the binder that was found in the yard, Amanda realized that it was _____ .

An **Objective Pronoun** is either the receiver of the action of the verb or the object of a preposition.

Example (1): He tripped him during the race.
"He" is a nominative pronoun, subject of the verb "tripped".
"Him" is an objective pronoun because it is the object of the sentence and receives the action of the verb.

Example (2): He gave the prize to him for winning the race.
"He" is a nominative pronoun, subject of the verb "gave".
"Him" is the object of the preposition "to" and therefore takes the objective case.

Exercise B

Place the proper case of pronoun in the space provided for each sentence.

1. We received a message from _____ (them, they).

2. She gave _____ (we, us) a phone call.

3. To _____ (who, whom) are you speaking?

4. The teacher gave _____ (her, she) an award.

5. The player passed the ball to _____ (him, he).

6. Please let _____ (me, I) join in your game.

7. The teacher asked to speak to _____ (she, her) in private.

A **Possessive Pronoun** shows ownership. There are singular and plural forms of possession for a pronoun.

Exercise C

Place the correct possessive form of the pronoun in each sentence.

1. She brought _____ dog to school.

2. John plays _____ guitar every night.

3. The students in grade four have _____ own playground.

4. We enjoyed _____ vacation.

5. You have found _____ but I have lost _____ .

Interrogative Pronouns ask questions. **Who, What, Which, Whose** are examples of interrogative pronouns.

Exercise D

In the blanks, place the proper interrogative pronoun. Place a different pronoun for each blank space.

1. _____ of the ice cream flavours is your favourite?

2. _____ books did you borrow for summer reading?

3. _____ is knocking at the door?

4. _____ are you planning to go for your vacation?

Exercise E

Fill in each space with the proper case of pronoun to suit the antecedent noun.

Make sure the pronoun also agrees with the verb in the sentence.

THE CLASS TRIP

On Thursday the grade four class was scheduled to go on a school trip to the zoo. _1._____ (it, we) was located on the other side of the city. _2._____ (they, we) were asked to bring _3._____ (her, their) own lunch. _4._____ (theirs, their) teacher, Ms. Renaldo, asked each of _5._____ (they, them) to bring a notebook and a pen to write down facts about the animals. John lost his bus tickets so Ms. Renaldo gave _6._____ (her, him) two more of _7._____ (these, them). When _8._____ (they, you)

arrived, the students formed a line at the entrance to meet 9._____ (your, their) guide for the day. 10._____ (her, his) name was Peter and 11._____ (our, he) took 12._____ (us, them) to the African section first. The lions were asleep in 13._____ (theirs, their) den. The monkeys playfully swung among branches and seemed to want to entertain the students. 14._____ (they, it) even made faces at 15._____ (he, them) when 16._____ (they, us) got close to the fence. The teacher asked jokingly to 17._____ (whom, who) the monkeys were speaking.

CHALLENGE

Circle the pronoun in each sentence from both Column A and Column B. The pronoun in each of these sentences is wrong. Make a trade with a pronoun from the other column.

Be careful – there is only one match for each sentence.

The Pronoun Switch Game

Column A	Column B
1. John tied her shoe.	a. We helped themselves to the treats.
2. The boys kept the candy to ourselves.	b. Whom is at the door?
3. John wasn't sure to who he should call.	c. Cheryl hurt his foot.
4. The audience clapped our hands.	d. I walked home on our own.
5. We took my time getting here.	e. We raised their voices in the singing.

3 Adjectives

An **Adjective** is used to modify or describe a noun or a pronoun. It gives additional information about a noun such as its size, colour, shape, number, or type.

Examples: the **green** car, the **large** house, the **round** swimming pool, the **three** boys, the **professional** player, the **other** book, the **school** yard

Do not confuse adjectives and adverbs. Remember, an adverb modifies a verb – the action word – in a sentence.

Exercise A

Underline the adjectives in each of the following sentences. The number in parentheses ( ) after each sentence tells you the number of adjectives in the sentence.

1. The tall boy threw his baseball through the small window. (3)

2. The cold rain pelted down on the tired fishermen. (2)

3. When the snow was deep, the older children built huge snow forts. (4)

4. Thousands of bright stars lit up the dark sky. (2)

5. This adventure story is a favourite of the younger children. (3)

6. The little girls played a short but sweet melody. (3)

The **Comparative** form of an adjective is used to compare two nouns. To change an adjective to the comparative form, add **er** to the original (descriptive) adjective.
Example: John is tall**er** than Paul.

The **Superlative** form of an adjective is used to compare more than two nouns. To change the original (descriptive) adjective to the superlative form, add **est**.
Example: John is the tall**est** boy in his class.

If an adjective ends in a single consonant, double the final consonant and add "er", e.g. thin – thinner. If an adjective ends in a double consonant, just add "er", e.g. smart – smarter. If an adjective ends in a "y", change the "y" to "i" and add "er", e.g. juicy – juicier.

Fill in the chart with the comparative and superlative forms of the simple adjectives listed.

Simple	Comparative	Superlative
1. small		smallest
2. early	earlier	
3. happy		
4. sad		
5. cheap		
6. fine		
7. kind		
8. new		

Some adjectives do not follow the rules above for changing to the comparative and superlative forms.

Exercise C

Complete the chart using the comparative and superlative forms.

Use some of the given adjectives more than once in the chart below.

worse   less   more
most   worst   best   good
more   some   least

Simple	Comparative	Superlative
1.	better	
2. much		
3. bad		
4.		most
5. little		

For many **adjectives with two or more syllables**, we place "more" or "less" before the simple adjective when comparing two things.

Examples: Her dog was **more intelligent** than mine.
He was the **less tired** of the two runners.

For the superlative form, "most" or "least" may be added to the adjective.

Examples: They watched the **most exciting** game.
This was the **least difficult** of the questions.

Exercise D

Circle the proper comparative or superlative form for each adjective below.

1. healthy   a. healthier   b. more healthier
2. beautiful   a. beautifullest   b. most beautiful
3. smart   a. smarter   b. more smarter
4. interesting   a. more interesting   b. interestinger
5. nice   a. nicest   b. most nice
6. happy   a. less happiest   b. least happy

Nouns as Adjectives

Sometimes a noun will be used like an adjective to modify (describe) another noun.

Example: chicken soup

The word "chicken" is a noun but it is acting as an adjective because it describes the kind of soup.

Exercise E

Match each noun/adjective in Column A with the noun it could describe.

Column A

1. New York ( )
2. space ( )
3. movie ( )
4. chocolate ( )
5. school ( )
6. family ( )
7. television ( )
8. football ( )

Column B

A. programme
B. team
C. star
D. station
E. sundae
F. City
G. yard
H. member

Exercise 7

Fill in the blanks with adjectives selected from the words below that make sense in the sentences.

Read all the words first; cross them off as you use them.

spacious	bus	cool	wise	hottest	No Swimming
disappointed	most	public	local		

A Day at the Beach

Because it was the 1._____ day of the year, the

camp counsellors made the 2._____ decision to go to

the 3._____ beach. They gave each camper a

4._____ ticket for the trip. The campers were

5._____ anxious to jump into the 6._____

lake water. However, when they arrived there was a

7._____ sign posted. The 8._____ campers

thought that they would have to go back to the camp. Luckily,

there was a 9._____ swimming pool nearby. Soon all

the campers were cooling off in the 10._____ swimming

pool.

4 Adverbs

An **Adverb** is a word that describes (modifies) a verb (action word).
An adverb can also modify an adjective and another adverb in a sentence.
Adverbs answer the questions "where", "when", "how", and "how much".
Adverbs often end in "ly".

Exercise A

Underline the adverbs in the following sentences. Indicate in the space provided whether the adverbs describe where, when, how, or how much.

1. The boys swam <u>swiftly</u>.   _____how_____

2. The girl spoke loudly so that everyone could hear her.   _____

3. It always rains when we have a baseball game.   _____

4. The teacher asked the students to come quickly to the gymnasium.   _____

5. He walked slowly down the street.   _____

6. He soon arrived home.   _____

7. The student spoke sincerely about her family.   _____

8. He shot the puck accurately at the net and quickly scored a goal.   _____ _____

9. The students worked busily at their history assignment.   _____

10. The older boy ran faster than the younger boy who ran farther.   _____ _____

11. The player was slightly hurt when the ball hit him.   _____

Forming Adverbs

Adverbs can be formed by adding "ly" or "ily" to a word.

Examples: greed – greed**ily**   happy – happ**ily**   sad – sad**ly**

If the original word ends in "y", drop the "y" and add "ily" to change that word to an adverb.

Example: happy – happ**ily**

Exercise B

Change the following words to adverbs. Place the adverb form in the space provided.

1. entire _____
2. greedy _____
3. fair _____
4. simple _____
5. sloppy _____
6. happy _____
7. desperate _____
8. nice _____
9. silent _____
10. weary _____

In some cases an adverb will modify an adjective instead of modifying a verb (action word).

Example: He was **pleasantly tired** after the workout.
"Pleasantly" is an adverb modifying the adjective "tired".

An adverb can also modify another adverb.

Example: He played **remarkably** well.
"Remarkably" is an adverb modifying the adverb "well".

Exercise C

Underline the adverbs that are modifying adjectives and other adverbs in the sentences below. Place parentheses ( ) around the adjectives or adverbs being modified.

1. The boat drifted lazily along.
2. The candy was sickly sweet.
3. The campers woke incredibly early.
4. The students were not entirely pleased with their test results.
5. The desperately hungry boy ate a huge lunch.
6. It was a fairly dark night.
7. The badly injured athlete was carried off the field.
8. The completely useless tool was thrown away.

To form a **Comparative Adverb**, place the word "more" before the adverb; to form the **Superlative** form of an adverb, place the word "most" before the adverb.

Examples: He writes clearly. He writes **more clearly** than his friend writes.
They treated us kindly. They treated us **most kindly**.

Exercise D

Rewrite the sentences below using the appropriate adverb form.

1. He rides his bicycle carefully than his brother.

   _____

2. He played hockey skilfully than all his team-mates.

   _____

3. The dogs in the cage barked viciously than the dogs on leashes.

   _____

4. The librarian spoke enthusiastically than our teacher about the book.

   _____

5. Her homework was carefully done than mine.

   _____

Some **Irregular Adverbs** change completely when becoming either comparative or superlative in form.
Examples: He swims **well**. He swims **better**. He swims **best**.

Exercise E

Fill in the blanks with the proper comparative and superlative forms of the following adverbs. Choose the correct words from the list below.

worse   better   best   worst

Adverb	Comparative	Superlative
1. bad		
2. well		
3. badly		

Exercise F

Fill in the blanks with the suitable adverbs provided.

Some blanks may require comparative or superlative adverb forms.

A Day at the Baseball Game

generously   kindly
wildly   dangerously
easily   vigorously
excitedly   finally
incredibly

We 1._____ hopped into the car to go to the

Saturday afternoon baseball game at the SkyDome. When we

2._____ arrived, the Toronto Blue Jays were

3._____ warming up on the field before the game.

The usher 4._____ allowed us to ask for autographs.

Most players offered 5._____ to sign our programmes.

When the players took the field to begin the game, we cheered

6._____ . The first batter avoided a pitch that was

7._____ close to his head. Then, with a sudden

explosive swing, he drove the ball 8._____ out of the

park. The Blue Jays went on to win 9._____ over the

opposition.

5 Verbs

A **Verb** is a word or group of words that shows the action in a sentence. It is the action performed by the subject (or object) of a sentence.

Examples: Paul **runs** across the street.
They **sailed** around the lake.
The people **were gathering** in front of the bus stop.

Exercise A

Underline the verbs in the following sentences.

> The number following each sentence tells you how many verbs are in it.

1. The children were playing in the park. (1)

2. The school principal made an announcement over the P.A. system. (1)

3. When he arrived home, he phoned a friend. (2)

4. The school bell rang loudly and the students began to line up. (2)

5. The dogs ran around the yard while the cat sat in the window and watched. (3)

A **Transitive Verb** is an action word that requires an object. An object is the receiver of the action of the verb.

Example: The girl **carried** her books.

The word "carried" is the verb and the word "books" is the object of the verb, that is, the thing that is being carried.

An **Intransitive Verb** does not require an object to complete its meaning.
Examples: She **laughed** at the joke.
He **rowed** across the river.

Exercise B

In each of the following sentences, underline the transitive verbs and place parentheses ( ) around the objects that receive the action of these verbs.

1. The parents applauded the performance of the play.

2. He shot the puck into the net.

3. The girls in the class sang a song while the boys performed a dance.

4. The bus driver took the passengers' tickets before leaving the depot.

5. The children played baseball in the schoolyard while the teachers held a meeting.

Exercise C

Place "T" for transitive and "I" for intransitive after each sentence. Underline the verb in each sentence.

1. The coach asked the players to try harder.   _____

2. Don't ask questions.   _____

3. The night sky was bright with stars.   _____

4. The horses raced around the track.   _____

5. He played a new game on his computer.   _____

 Auxiliary Verbs help the main verbs in a sentence. The following words are often used as auxiliary verbs: may, be, shall, will, might, must, have, has, and can.

Examples: She **may** eat her dinner in the living room.
The boys **will** play hockey after school.
Everyone **has** been helpful.
She **has** walked all the way home.

Exercise D

Write the proper auxiliary verb in each space provided.

1. The young girl _____ (will, was) help her mother when she needs it.

2. The ocean tide _____ (have, has) moved farther out.

3. He _____ (did, will) go to the game if he can get a ticket.

4. The students _____ (must, might) obey the rules of the school to avoid getting into trouble.

5. They _____ (have, will) take a trip if they can get time off work.

Parts of a Verb

In English there are four main parts of most verbs: present, present participle, past, past participle.

The **present tense** (form) of the verb is the basic form.

The **past tense** is the form that shows that the action of the verb has already occurred. The past tense is usually formed by adding "ed" or "d" to the basic form.

The **present participle** form of a verb is formed by adding "ing" to the basic verb.

The **past participle** may have the same form as that of the past tense.

Examples: present tense – cross, do, go, walk
present participle – crossing, doing, going, walking
past tense – crossed, did, went, walked
past participle – crossed, done, gone, walked

Note: The verb "go" is irregular and its past tense form is "went".

Exercise E

Fill in the proper form of the verbs in the chart that match the form provided. The first one is done for you.

The past participle and the past tense are often the same.

Basic Form	Past Tense	Present Participle	Past Participle
1. begin	began	beginning	begun
2. catch			
3.		cutting	
4. become			
5. draw			drawn
6.		knowing	
7.	heard		
8. read			
9.		wearing	
10.	wrote		
11.		going	
12. bite			
13.			sung

Exercise 7

Place the proper form of the verb in parentheses ( ) in the space provided for each sentence below.

1. The athletes from our school _____ (was, were) gathering in front of the school to _____ (organize, organized) themselves for the track and field competition.

2. After the bus had _____ (arrive, arrived), we were finally on our way.

3. When our athletes _____ (arriving, arrived) at the stadium, many teams _____ (have, had) been _____ (prepare, preparing) for the events.

4. Our 200 metre runner, Paul, _____ (feel, felt) that he had a good chance to win his race.

5. Our school had _____ (training, trained) very hard for this competition.

6. Our relay team was _____ (running, ran) in the inside lane.

7. Paul _____ (comes, came) second in the 200-metre race, and our relay team had _____ (placing, placed) first.

8. Everyone was very proud of the victory, and the relay team _____ (ran, running) a victory lap around the track.

9. When it was time for the 100-metre race, the runners were _____ (taken, taking) their marks _____ (waited, waiting) for the gun to go off.

10. After a fierce race, our runner _____ (finished, finishing) third.

6 The Sentence

A **Sentence** is a group of words that expresses a complete thought.

A **Simple Sentence** is made up of a subject and a predicate. The subject (usually a noun) performs an action; the predicate, which includes a verb, describes the action.

Example: The boy threw the ball to his friend.
  subject – the boy   bare subject (noun) – boy
  predicate – threw the ball to his friend   bare predicate (verb) – threw

Exercise A

For each sentence below draw a line separating the subject and predicate, and draw a line under the bare subject (noun) and the bare predicate (verb).

1. John watched a movie with his friends.

2. The tired travellers waited at the bus terminal.

3. Most swimmers fear the presence of sharks.

4. Canada is the largest country in the world.

5. He will take his bicycle with him on holiday.

6. It is a beautiful day today.

Compound Subjects and Compound Verbs

In a simple sentence it is possible to have two or more subjects (compound) and two or more verbs.

Example (1): **Peter and Paul** are brothers.
    The compound subjects are joined by the conjunction "and".

Example (2): The puppy likes to **run and jump** around the yard.
    The compound verbs are joined by the conjunction "and".

Exercise B

Unscramble each group of words below to form sentences with a compound subject, a compound verb, or both.

1. horses   barn   shared   the   and   cows   the

_____

2. cried   time   the   same   she   and   at   laughed

_____

3. red   and   are   favourite   colours   her   blue   yellow

_____

4. chewed   his   swallowed   food   he   and   digested

_____

5. carried   the   packed   and   boxes   girls   the   boys   and

_____

6. or   Maria   babysit   tonight   Joanna   will

_____

7. clothes   Janet   this   washed   the   morning   dried   and

_____

8. see   hens   some   I   and   there   can   over   ducks

_____

Verb Agreement

In a sentence, the subject and verb must agree. A single subject requires the singular form of the verb; a compound subject requires the plural form of the verb.

Examples: His mother **is** working late tonight. (singular)
His mother and father **are** working late tonight. (plural)

Exercise C

In each sentence, change the verb in parentheses ( ) to match the subject.

1. She _____ (have) a new car.

2. John and Peter _____ (likes) to play hockey.

3. Eric _____ (want) to buy a new pair of running shoes.

4. Susan, Ashley, and Dayna _____ (is) in the same class.

5. Lauren and Kara _____ (was) the last to leave the party.

6. Children _____ (plays) in the schoolyard.

7. Jessica and I _____ (am) good friends.

When two simple sentences are joined together with a conjunction (and, or, but, if...), then a **Compound Sentence** is formed.

Example: The children were caught in the rain and they didn't have umbrellas.

Note the joining word (conjunction) "and" which joins the two simple sentences.

Exercise D

Match the sentences in Column A with those in Column B forming compound sentences that make sense. Write the compound sentence that you have formed by connecting the sentences with a joining word (conjunction).

so	if	and	but

Column A

1. School was cancelled
2. It was her birthday
3. The weather was awful
4. We would be rewarded with treats
5. The fishermen waited patiently
6. They will be late
7. The children played a vigorous game of soccer
8. The boys were hungry

Column B

• they didn't catch a thing
• they miss the train
• we played outside anyway
• the students went home
• there was nothing for them to eat
• she opened her presents
• they were all very tired
• we did all our work

1. _____
2. _____
3. _____
4. _____
5. _____
6. _____
7. _____
8. _____

Incomplete Sentences

A sentence must convey a complete thought in order for it to make sense to the reader.

Example: When I was walking home

This is not a complete sentence because it needs more information for it to make sense.

When I was walking home, I met my friend, Kyle.

Notice that with the additional information – "I met my friend Kyle" – the sentence now makes sense.

Incomplete sentences such as the one in the example above are called **Fragments**.

Exercise E

Imagine that you are either a spectator at the school play or one of the actors in the play. Complete the sentences below telling a story about your experience with the school play.

The School Play

1.   When the curtain went up, _____

2.   During the first scene, _____

3.   _____ because the costumes were too warm.

4.   _____ when the lights went dim.

5.   If you forget your lines, _____

6.   Because it was the first school play, _____

7.   _____ even after many rehearsals.

8.   Although some people were nervous, _____

9.   When the play was finished, _____

7 Building Sentences with Descriptors

The basic sentence is made up of two parts: a subject and a predicate.

To make a sentence more interesting and to add important information to a sentence, descriptors can be added.

Descriptors include adjectives, adverbs, adjective phrases, and adverb phrases.

Example: Here is a basic sentence with a subject and a predicate.
The girl ran home.
Here is the same sentence with an adjective and an adverb.
The **happy** girl ran home **quickly**.

Exercise A

Make each of the following sentences more interesting by adding an adjective to describe the subject and an adverb to describe the verb. Choose from the adjective/adverb word pairs to fill in the blanks in each sentence below.

Use both words in each pair for each sentence below.

puffy, lazily   hot, mercilessly   French, quietly
brave, fearlessly   young, gracefully   best, kindly
vicious, fiercely   reckless, dangerously

1. The _____ teacher _____ called out our names.

2. His _____ dog barked _____ at the people passing by.

3. The _____ clouds drifted _____ overhead.

4. The _____ sun beat down _____ on the sunbathers.

5. The _____ ballerina danced _____ on the stage.

6. The _____ stuntman jumped _____ from the top of the building.

7. The _____ firefighter _____ entered the burning building.

8. Her _____ friend _____ offered to help her clean her room.

A **Phrase** is a group of words that acts as a single word in a sentence. Unlike sentences and clauses, phrases do not contain a subject and a predicate.

An **Adjective Phrase** acts as an adjective and describes a noun.

Example: The hat in the box was a gift for his mother.
"In the box" is an adjective phrase because it gives information about the hat.

An **Adverb Phrase** acts as an adverb and describes a verb.

Example: He placed his mother's hat in the box.
"In the box" is an adverb phrase because it tells where the hat was placed.

Adverb phrases often answer the questions where and when.

Exercise B

In the space following each sentence, write "ADV" (adverb) or "ADJ" (adjective) to indicate which type of phrase is used. Underline the preposition that introduces each phrase.

1. The children played *in the school yard* during recess. _____

2. They played a game *of baseball* called "workups". _____

3. Their game was interrupted by the ringing *of the bell*. _____

4. The team *with the most runs* when the bell rang was the winner. _____

5. John is the best baseball player *in our school*. _____

6. He once hit the ball *over the schoolyard fence*. _____

7. Mr. Wright, the grade four teacher, picks even teams *of twelve players*. _____

8. He said that one day we could play a team *from another school*. _____

9. He said that the game would take place *at the community baseball diamond*. _____

10. We are hoping to arrange to play this game *in the spring*. _____

Exercise C

Underline the phrases in the sentences below. Sometimes one phrase follows another.

There are 16 phrases in the 10 sentences below, but one sentence does not have a phrase at all!

1. They rode their bikes across the field and over the hill.
2. In the summertime, his family rents a cottage by a small lake.
3. If the teacher asks a question, he will give the answer in the textbook.
4. At the beginning of our gym class, the teacher checks our uniforms.
5. He stood up in front of the class and read a poem.
6. After we ate lunch, we organized games in the gymnasium.
7. We placed our books under our desks during the test.
8. Our umbrellas were useful when the rain came down.
9. We let the dog in the house because it was cold in the doghouse.
10. The campers pitched their tents in the clearing and cooked supper on the campfire.

Exercise D

Create a descriptive paragraph by using as many of the phrases given below as possible. Add your own descriptive phrases to the sentences that you are composing.

Perhaps you could organize your sentences in a rough draft first.

A Daytrip to the Beach

in the sand   in the car   on Lake Ontario   with my family
in the water   after our picnic   during the drive home
at the gas station   to the beach   on a daytrip
in the hot sun   after breakfast   on July 22

_____

_____

_____

_____

_____

_____

_____

Verbal Phrases begin with the participle form of a verb which ends in "ing". Skiing, running, jumping, singing are all verbals.

When a verbal is used as a noun, it is called a gerund.

Example: **Skiing** is her favourite sport.

When a verbal involves a group of words, it becomes a verbal phrase.

Example: **Skiing in the mountains** is her favourite activity.

CHALLENGE

At the beginning of each sentence below is a verbal. Add words to that verbal to make a verbal phrase and a complete sentence.

1. Swimming ____in cool water____ is refreshing.

2. Laughing _____ is not polite.

3. Singing _____ is her after-school activity.

4. Throwing _____ with a partner is fun.

5. Running _____ is their everyday exercise.

6. Playing _____ is a favourite of school children.

7. Enjoying _____ is a good family activity.

8. Exercising _____ is good for your health.

9. Helping _____ is a nice thing to do.

Progress Test 1

Nouns

There may be more than one noun in each row.

Exercise A

Circle the nouns in each row of words below.

1. walking   sidewalk   walked   waking   walker
2. glad   happy   sad   sadness   happiness
3. before   after   afternoon   morning   mourn
4. children   childish   childlike   infant   child
5. unusual   strange   stranger   weird   different

Exercise B

Underline the proper nouns in each row below.

There may be more than one proper noun in each row. Capital letters have been removed from the proper nouns for test purposes.

1. mount everest   mountains   mountainous   location
2. john   boy   friend   classmate
3. june   month   date   july
4. ottawa   ottawa river   riverbank   ocean
5. disneyland   studio   amusement park   recreation
6. hockey   the toronto maple leafs   professionals   nhl

Exercise C

Write the plural or singular form of each noun in the space.

Singular	Plural		Singular	Plural
1.	oxen	5.	wife	
2. mouse		6.	life	
3. fish		7.	tooth	
4.	children	8.		feet

Pronouns

Exercise D

Write the possessive form, the plural form, and the possessive form of the plural for each pronoun.

Pronoun	Possessive	Plural	Possessive
1. I			
2. she			
3. it			
4. you			

Adjectives

Exercise E

Circle the adjective form in each row of words below.

1. beauty   beautiful   beautify
2. wear   weary   wearing
3. care   careful   careless
4. large   big   enormous
5. gold   golden   bracelet
6. precious   valuable   diamond

There may be more than one adjective form in each row.

Exercise F

Underline the proper comparative or superlative form for each adjective below.

1. large ⟶   a. most larger   b. more larger   c. larger
2. huge ⟶   a. hugest   b. most hugest   c. most huger
3. lucky ⟶   a. luckier   b. more luckiest   c. luckierest
4. fine ⟶   a. most finer   b. more finest   c. finest
5. bad ⟶   a. worse   b. more badder   c. baddest

Progress Test 1

Adverbs

Exercise G

Underline the adverb form in each row below.

1. happy   happily   happiness
2. careless   careful   carelessly
3. quickly   quickness   quick
4. creative   creatively   creation
5. final   finished   finally

Verbs

Exercise H

Three sentences below have two verbs.

Underline the verb in each sentence below.

1. The boys chased after the dog that picked up their ball.

2. The rain poured down on the parade.

3. You laughed at the joke but it wasn't funny.

4. Richard and Michael ate their lunches and drank their milk in the park.

5. Swimming and running are good exercises.

Exercise I

Underline the verb(s) in each sentence and write "T" for transitive and "I" for intransitive in the spaces provided.

Transitive verbs require an object – a receiver of the action of the verb. Intransitive verbs do not require an object to complete the meaning of a sentence.

1. The Toronto Maple Leafs play in the Air Canada Centre.   ____

2. She chose the dress that she would wear for her birthday party.   ____ ____

3. The teacher gave us a talk about caring about the feelings of others.   ____

4. When he was speaking, we listened attentively.   ____ ____

5. The clouds covered the sky while the wind blew.   ____ ____

Exercise J

From the choices for each sentence, write the appropriate auxiliary (helping) verb in the space provided.

1. We _____ (will, were) walking home together after school.
2. The boat _____ (have, had) drifted out to the middle of the lake.
3. They _____ (could, have) take a trip this summer.
4. The children _____ (must, has) eat their lunch in the cafeteria.
5. She _____ (will, had) play after school tomorrow.

Exercise K

Write the appropriate past tense for each verb below in the space provided.

1. draw _____
2. see _____
3. catch _____
4. write _____
5. think _____
6. read _____
7. drive _____
8. has _____
9. do _____
10. cry _____

Sentences

Exercise L

Draw a line between the subject and the predicate of each sentence below. Underline the bare subject and the bare predicate in each sentence.

1. The team played football in the old stadium beside the river.
2. Both the boys and the girls used the same playing field during recess.
3. The audience laughed when they watched the funny movie.
4. We wear our gloves whenever it gets very cold.
5. The tall boys played basketball after school.
6. It rains whenever we plan a picnic.

Exercise M

The following sentences have either compound subjects, compound verbs, or both. Unscramble the sentences and underline the compound subjects and verbs.

1. and   Mike   Janet   laughed   sang   and

   _____

2. game   we   baseball   ate   the   peanuts   popcorn   and   at

   _____

3. at   same   the   laughed   we   and   cried   time

   _____

4. created   presented   they   and   together   project   the

   _____

5. jumped   water   the   children   in   splashed   and   the

   _____

Exercise N

Change the verb in parentheses ( ) to agree with the subject in each of the sentences below. Put the correct verb in the space provided.

1. Paul _____ (want) to be the captain of the team.

2. Most of the students _____ (enjoys) creating artwork.

3. They _____ (carrying) their report cards home in envelopes.

4. Can't we _____ (gone) to the movies on Sunday afternoon?

5. Lucy _____ (giggling) too often in class, and the teacher _____ (are) not pleased.

6. Linda and Karen _____ (driven) to the store to shop for groceries.

7. Sam's uncle always _____ (make) funny jokes.

8. The drive to the cottage _____ (take) about two hours.

Adjective and Adverb Phrases

Exercise O

Underline the phrase in each sentence below and write "ADV" or "ADJ" in the space provided. If the sentence has more than one phrase, underline both and state the type of phrase in the order that they appear in the sentence.

> Each of these types of phrases begins with a preposition such as in, of, at, under, below, and before.

1. The door of the house was left open in the morning. _____ _____

2. Outside the window, a Blue Jay landed on a branch. _____ _____

3. In the evening, we went for a drive to town. _____ _____ _____

4. The car in the parking lot received a ticket. _____

5. The students of grade four were playing in the gymnasium. _____ _____

6. At the bottom of the pool sat the goggles of the polo player. _____ _____ _____

Exercise P

Underline the gerunds or verbal phrases in the sentences below. Write "G" for gerund or "VP" for verbal phrase in the space following each sentence.

> #3, 4, and 6 have either two gerunds or verbal phrases or one of each.

1. Swimming is my favourite summer activity. _____

2. Hiking in the mountains can be adventurous. _____

3. Looking in store windows can be interesting and cheaper than spending money. _____ _____

4. Singing and dancing are skills needed to be in the school play. _____ _____

5. I enjoy walking in the rain. _____

6. Skiing is fun but tobogganing down the hills is more exciting. _____ _____

8 Prepositions and Conjunctions

A **Preposition** is a word that connects nouns and pronouns to other parts of a sentence.

A **Phrase** is a group of words that describes a noun or a verb. Phrases begin with prepositions.

Example: He placed his book **in** the desk.

"In" is a preposition that introduces the phrase "in the desk". The phrase tells us where the book is placed.

Exercise A

Can you pick out the prepositions in the sentences below? Underline the prepositions in each sentence.

1. The students went <u>to</u> the gym <u>after</u> school.

2. He placed his feet under the table.

3. The child went down the slide.

4. He slept during the movie.

5. They swam across the lake.

The first one is done for you.

6. He was a cousin of mine.

7. He had to choose between cookies and cake.

8. The park was near the bus stop.

9. She did her homework without any help.

10. He waited inside the house for the rain to stop.

Exercise B

Below are some common prepositions. Use each one in your own sentence.

about	behind	onto	over	except	through

1. _____

2. _____

3. _____

4. _____

5. _____

6. _____

Prepositional Phrases

Often a preposition is followed by a noun or pronoun. We refer to that noun or pronoun as the **object** of the preposition.

A phrase that connects to a noun is an adjective phrase because, like an adjective, it describes that noun.

A phrase that connects to a verb is an adverb phrase because it modifies the verb it is connected to.

Example: The dog **in the yard** was barking.

The preposition "in" connects the phrase "in the yard" to the noun "dog". Therefore it is an adjective phrase. The word "yard" would be the object of the preposition "in".

Exercise C

Underline the phrase in each of the following sentences. In the space provided after each sentence, write "ADJ" if it is an adjective phrase, and "ADV" if it is an adverb phrase.

1. The cars raced <u>in a circle</u>.   ADV

2. The clouds in the sky threatened rain.   _____

3. The members of the team sat together.   _____

4. The sign over the doorway was lit up.   _____

5. The children sang in the choir.   _____

6. The horses ran around the track.   _____

7. Since yesterday he has been sleeping.   _____

8. He cannot play for the school team.   _____

9. She searched throughout the house for her jacket. _____

10. The students of grade four enjoy doing homework. _____

11. I have new friends since yesterday.   _____

Exercise D

Complete each sentence with an adjective or adverb phrase.

> The prepositions are italicized.

1. The boys went swimming *in* _____the river_____ .

2. We looked at the fish *in* _____ .

3. Place your boots *on* _____ .

4. The players *on* _____ celebrated the victory.

5. He arrived *at* _____ .

6. Do you like to play *in* _____ ?

7. The teachers *at* _____ are very strict.

A **Conjunction** connects words or groups of words.

Some familiar conjunctions are: **and   but   or   yet   nor   so   but**

Example: You **and** I are best friends.

Exercise E

Complete each of the following sentences by creating details to follow the conjunction. The conjunctions are italicized.

1. I called at your home *but* ____you were not there____ .

2. Pop *and* _____ make for a tasty treat.

3. It rained all night *but* _____ .

4. Either you come to my house *or* _____ .

5. I will help you *if* _____ .

6. Either he is laughing *or* _____ .

7. We will go to the beach *and* _____ .

8. Snow *and* _____ make for poor driving conditions.

9. We will go on holiday, come rain *or* _____ .

A **Subordinating Conjunction** joins an independent clause (a sentence) with a dependent clause. A dependent clause needs additional information for it to be complete.

Example: **While** I was walking to school, I found some money.

"I found some money" is an independent clause (complete sentence).

"While I was walking to school" is a dependent clause because it is incomplete on its own.

Exercise 7

Combine each pair of clauses by using the subordinating conjunction in parentheses ( ).

1. You can show me a better way / I will do it my own way   (unless)

   _____

2. She was the oldest / she made all the rules   (because)

   _____

3. We played the entire game / we were very tired   (even though)

   _____

4. You are sure this is the right way to go / we will follow you   (if)

   _____

5. I was talking on the phone / Sophia was watching a cartoon   (while)

   _____

CHALLENGE

There is a word missing in each of the incorrect sentences below. Can you figure out what is missing and add the word needed? Place your word in the space provided.

1. Baseball a great summer game.   _____

2. I caught a fish I was sleeping in the boat.   _____

3. A needle in a haystack is hard find.   _____

9 Building Complex Sentences

An **Independent Clause** is a group of words containing a subject and a verb that expresses a complete idea. Another name for the independent clause is the **Simple Sentence**.

The **Dependent Clause** is often referred to as a **Subordinate Clause**. It is dependent because, although it has a subject and a verb, it needs more information to make it complete. A dependent clause cannot stand alone; it needs the help of an independent clause (simple sentence).

Exercise A

Decide which kind of clause each group of words represents, and write the type of clause in the space provided.

There are 6 dependent clauses below.

1. Before the game started. _____

2. Whenever we go to our cottage. _____

3. It rained the entire time. _____

4. Instead of playing basketball. _____

5. My friends and I like to ride bikes. _____

6. Her dog chases cars, but always comes when called. _____

7. In the early morning sunlight. _____

8. The school emptied when the fire alarm sounded. _____

9. While we were waiting for the bus. _____

10. Since you asked for my help. _____

Exercise B

Underline the independent clause in each of the complex sentences below.

1. Whenever we go to the movies, we buy popcorn.

2. She told us to wait until we all finished our homework.

3. If the weather is clear, we can have a barbecue.

4. After we watch our favourite television show, we go right to bed.

5. Once the bell rings, recess is over.

6. He is happy now that his bike is fixed.

7. As long as we live close by, we can walk to school.

8. The students practised running when it was track and field season.

9. Because she was late for class, she had to go to the office first.

10. My father was looking forward to the holidays because he could take time off work.

Complex Sentences

When a dependent clause is joined to an independent clause by a subordinating conjunction, a complex sentence is formed.

Some of the most frequently used subordinating conjunctions are: **because, although, unless, whenever, after, as, as if, before, wherever, until**...

Exercise C

Make a complex sentence by putting a dependent clause in the space following the subordinating conjunction in each of the sentences below.

Make sure the clause has a "subject" and a "verb". Do not construct phrases.

1. *If* _____ , I will gladly help you.

2. He said he would meet me *when* _____ .

3. I will do *whatever* _____ .

4. She invited me to her house *after* _____ .

5. *If* _____ , we will celebrate.

6. *Until* _____ , I had never been to a circus.

7. We went on holiday *when* _____ .

8. The teacher asked us to finish our work *before* _____ .

9. Meet me in the school yard *when* _____ .

10. I asked my friend to tell me *where* _____ .

Combine the following choppy sentences into longer sentences.

You might have to change the order of the clauses or begin the sentence with the subordinating conjunction.

Example:

I enjoy eating candy. I go to the movies. (when)

When I go to the movies, I enjoy eating candy.   or

I enjoy eating candy when I go to the movies.

1.   We went back to school. It was Monday. (because)

2.   The school play was cancelled. Most of the participants were taken ill. (when)

3.   The rain ended. The sun came out. (after)

4.   We waited for hours. The bus finally came. (until)

5.   The postman brought the mail. It was nearly noon hour. (when)

6.   We began to do our work. The morning announcements were made. (after)

7.   We get very tired. We have basketball practice. (whenever)

8.   We are allowed. We will go to the game after school. (if)

Using Verbals

In an earlier unit, we learnt a verb form called gerund which ends in "ing". Gerunds are verbals that are used as nouns in a sentence.

Example (1): **Running** is a vigorous activity.

In this example, the **subject** of the sentence is "running" which is a verbal.

Example (2): He enjoys **running** with his team-mates.

In this case, "running" is an **object**. It is what he enjoys doing. "He" is the subject of the sentence, and "running" is the object.

Exercise D

Underline the gerund in each sentence below and state in the space whether it is the subject or the object.

1. Skiing can be dangerous. _____

2. We like biking along the mountain trails. _____

3. There is nothing better than eating ice cream on a hot day. _____

4. We all picked swimming as our favourite cottage activity. _____

Verbals instead of Dependent Clauses

A verbal can replace a long dependent clause and make the sentence easier to read.

Example: **While he was running** for the bus, he tripped and fell.   becomes
Running for the bus, he tripped and fell.

Exercise E

Finish each sentence below by replacing the dependent clause with a verbal.

1. When he was skiing down the hill, he fell.

   He fell _____ .

2. When she was playing with the toys, she was happy.

   _____ , she was happy.

3. While he was listening to music, he started to dance.

   _____ , he started to dance.

10 Relative Clauses

The Restrictive Relative Clause

A restrictive clause (also called defining clause) gives necessary information to the sentence, particularly in defining or modifying a noun or verb.

Example: The boy arrived at school today. (no clause)

The boy who was new to the school arrived at school today. (restrictive clause)

The clause "who was new to the school" adds important information to describe the noun, boy.

Note that the restrictive clause is not separated from the rest of the sentence by commas.

Relative pronouns are used to introduce relative clauses. The common relative pronouns are: who, what, whom, whose, which, that, where, when, why.

Exercise A

Underline the restrictive relative clause in each of the sentences below.

1. The teachers who were located on the lower floor complained of cold classrooms.

2. The park where we used to play hide-and-seek is no longer there.

3. Textbooks that are no longer used were sent to needy countries.

4. Animals that are facing extinction must be protected.

5. The parents whose children took the school bus were asked to register.

6. The teacher rewarded the person who scored the highest results in the test.

Exercise B

Add your own restrictive relative clauses to make the sentences below more interesting.

1. The game was finally played.

   The game that was delayed by rain was finally played.

2. The children went for a cool dip in the swimming pool.

   _____

3. Her house was difficult to find.

_____

4. The dog barked loudly.

_____

5. The house was hard to get to.

_____

6. The hockey team was unbeatable.

_____

7. People crowded outside the ticket office.

_____

Exercise C

Complete the following sentences that have restrictive relative clauses.

1. The words that were spoken by the student _____

2. The barn which was home to the cows _____

3. Birds that fly south for the winter _____

4. She wanted a car that was reliable _____

5. The bus that picks us up every morning _____

6. The student whose painting is displayed in the hallway _____

_____

Exercise D

Finish the sentences by completing the restrictive relative clauses.

1. The dog that _____ is fun to play with.

2. The dog belongs to the boy who _____ .

3. The tree which _____ is fun to climb.

4. He was laughing at the clown who _____ .

5. They bought the house that _____ .

6. The player whom _____ is my brother.

The Non-Restrictive Relative Clause (also called non-defining clause) gives information that is not necessary to the basic meaning of the sentence. This information often adds interest to the sentence. Note that a non-restrictive relative clause is set off, before and after, by commas.

Example: The house, which had yellow shutters, was their home for many years.

The non-restrictive clause "which had yellow shutters" is not essential to the understanding of the sentence. It simply adds additional information.

Exercise E

Underline the non-restrictive clauses in the following sentences and add commas.

1. The dog which had a fluffy white coat played in the park.

2. His friend who was very reliable joined in the games they were playing.

3. The student who wore a green coat stood in the cold waiting for the school bus.

4. Relatives many of whom I didn't recognize arrived from everywhere.

5. Her friend who lives on the same street went away for the holidays.

6. Discussions about the environment which we enjoy are usually interesting.

7. The vacation which came in March gave us a much needed break from school.

8. Students who were carrying their knapsacks hurried into the school.

9. The boy who was riding a bicycle stopped at the store to make a purchase.

Exercise F

Complete the non-restrictive relative clause in each sentence below.

1. The skater, who _____ , won the competition.

2. The idea, which _____ , was the solution to the problem.

3. His friend, who _____ , was a great addition to the team.

4. The letter, which _____ , contained the information.

5. My uniform, which _____ , was one size too big.

6. Sandy, whose _____ , also sings and dances well.

Exercise G

Add non-restrictive clauses to the following sentences to make them more interesting.

The bold words in the sentences below suggest where you might add your non-restrictive relative clauses.

1. The **girl** won the **race**.
   The girl, who wore the blue top, won the race. _____

2. The **people** assembled in front of the **court house**.

   _____

3. **Hot dogs** were served in the **park**.

   _____

4. His **hat** was found in the **schoolyard**.

   _____

5. My **uncle** took me to the **cottage**.

   _____

6. Before the **boy** spoke out in class, everything was quiet.

   _____

7. The **passengers** grew impatient waiting for the **next train**.

   _____

8. The **actors** took to the **stage**.

   _____

9. The **animals** looked hungry.

   _____

10. He bought a **coat** from the **sports store**.

    _____

11 Developing the Paragraph

A **Paragraph** is a group of sentences that expresses a common idea. It is made up of the following:

Topic sentence – introduces main idea
Body sentences – develop the main idea by adding information in logical order
Conclusion – summarizes topic; adds further thought; links to next paragraph

Exercise A

For each paragraph, choose the most appropriate topic sentence and write it in the space provided. Give a title to the paragraph as well.

Paragraph 1

Topic sentences:

- Puppies love to chase a ball.
- Lauren's birthday present was a fluffy, little pup.
- Dogs make good companions.

Title: _____

_____ . She got this puppy when it was only eight weeks old and named it Abbey. Abbey loves to chase a tennis ball around the yard. At night the puppy curls up on her bed and goes to sleep. Lauren has promised her parents that she will take very good care of her new puppy.

Paragraph 2

Topic sentences:

- Canada is a very large country.
- This summer, we will travel across Canada.
- Driving long distances can be tiring.

Title: _____

_____ . My father showed us the route we will take across Canada. It will take us seven days to reach

Vancouver from our home in Toronto. We will drive through five provinces including Ontario and British Columbia. We are excited because we have never travelled outside Ontario.

Paragraph 3

> **Topic sentences:**
>
> - With two out in the ninth inning, we were losing by one run.
> - A close score in baseball makes for an exciting finish.
> - Sometimes a baseball game goes into extra innings.

Title: _____

_____ . Randall was our last chance to tie the game. He was very nervous. With two strikes on him, he took one final swing at the ball and connected for a home run. At that point we evened the score, but we went on to lose in the first extra inning. Although our glory didn't last long, we had fun playing in such an exciting game.

Paragraph 4

> **Topic sentences:**
>
> - Birthdays are often celebrated by eating cake.
> - Kara had kept her birthday a secret from everyone at school except her best friend.
> - Lisa is Kara's best friend.

Title: _____

_____ . When everyone in the class stood up and sang "Happy Birthday To You", Kara was shocked and embarrassed. She had not told anyone about her birthday. Her friend, Lisa, brought a huge cake and everyone in the class had a slice. Once the shock wore off, Kara enjoyed the rest of her special day.

Organizing Sentences into a Paragraph

A paragraph begins with a topic sentence which introduces the main idea of the paragraph. The body of the paragraph is made up of sentences that give information about the main idea. They should be arranged in a logical order to best develop the main idea of the paragraph. Often, these sentences will appear in the order that events happen.

Exercise B

Arrange each group of sentences below into a well-organized paragraph. Write the letters in the spaces provided.

1. A. Raking these leaves can be tiring.
   B. Bags and bags of leaves will be filled before the winter arrives.
   C. If the leaves aren't raked, there will be a mess in the yard when the spring arrives.
   D. The fall is here and the leaves will fill our backyards.

1	2	3	4

2. A. I have just started to read the *Lord of the Rings* series of books.
   B. *Harry Potter* and *Lord of the Rings* are two of the most popular children's books.
   C. Many of my classmates have read all the books in both series.
   D. When I have finished that series, I will begin to read the *Harry Potter* series.

1	2	3	4

3. A. The lake water was cooler than expected.
   B. It was a hot summer day and we were anxious to cool off.
   C. We decided to take a dip on the lake nearby.
   D. However, we soon got used to the chilly water and felt refreshed.

1	2	3	4

Exercise C

For each topic sentence below, write a short paragraph of four sentences.

Make sure that your sentences give information about the main idea stated in the topic sentence. The last sentence should be a concluding thought.

1. After a long day of driving, we finally arrived at our hotel.

   _____

   _____

   _____

   _____

2. When my name was called to say my speech in front of the class, I was very nervous.

   _____

   _____

   _____

   _____

3. This summer I will earn extra money doing odd jobs in my neighbourhood.

   _____

   _____

   _____

   _____

4. My friends and I decided to put on a show at school for Parents' Night.

   _____

   _____

   _____

   _____

12 Rules of Punctuation

Punctuation Marks are symbols to help the reader better understand what is being written. They tell a reader when to pause, when a sentence ends, and when a sentence should be read with emphasis.

End Punctuation
1. A declarative sentence makes a simple statement of fact or information. It ends with a period (.).
2. An interrogative sentence asks a question. It ends with a question mark (?).
3. An imperative sentence gives an order. It ends with a period (.).
4. An exclamatory sentence shows emotion. It ends with an exclamation mark (!).

Exercise A

Of the six sentences below, four have incorrect end punctuation. Circle the number of the incorrectly punctuated sentences and make the necessary corrections.

1. Look out.
2. I wondered why they hadn't arrived yet?
3. What time did her party begin?
4. I would like all the grade four students to sit over here.
5. Never swim without supervision?
6. Ouch, that hurts.

> Be careful of sentences that seem to be emphatic but are really just simple statements.

> End punctuation such as the period has other grammatical uses. Periods are also the end punctuation for most abbreviations.

Exercise B

Write the abbreviation form of each of the following words and include the proper punctuation.

1. mister _____
2. United States _____
3. miss _____
4. in the afternoon _____
5. doctor _____
6. in the morning _____
7. British Columbia _____
8. Prince Edward Island _____
9. Newfoundland _____
10. company (i.e. business) _____

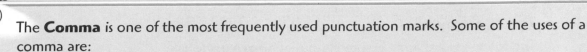

The **Comma** is one of the most frequently used punctuation marks. Some of the uses of a comma are:

1. To create a mild pause in a sentence – If you don't hurry, you will be late.
2. To separate items in a list – He likes to play baseball, soccer, tennis, football, and basketball.
3. To set off a subordinate clause – While he waited for a bus, he read his book.
4. To introduce and follow a quotation – Ashley said, "Wait for me after school."
   "Wait for me after school," said Ashley.
5. To set off introductory words and phrases – Well, you finally arrived.
6. To set off descriptions in apposition – My teacher, Miss Johnson, is new to our school.

Exercise C

There are many commas missing in the following paragraph. Place commas where you think they belong according to the rules above.

There are 24 missing commas.

The Championship Game

Monday after school we played basketball for the city championship. Our coach Mr. Phillips said "I want everyone to try their hardest today." When the referee threw up the jump ball the game had started. They missed their first shot and we took the ball the length of the court for our first score. We knew that if we didn't play defence we would lose. Each of us covered our man and we allowed them to score very few baskets. The spectators cheered screamed clapped and waved their arms during the game. Oddly enough the opposition managed to even the score in the last minute of play. The championship came down to the last play of the game and we had the ball.

Slowly carefully and with great care we brought the ball up the floor. Jamie our team captain called a time-out. We huddled around our coach and he said "Make sure the last shot is a good one." Jamie on a pass from Rick dribbled to the corner spun around and threw up a rather long shot. The coach was not happy when this happened. But much to our surprise the next sound we heard was "Swish".

The Apostrophe

The following are some common rules of **apostrophe** use:

1. Use an apostrophe to show possession.

Examples: We did this **week's** math quiz on Tuesday.
We ordered our food from the **children's** menu.
The **teachers'** staff room is upstairs.

2. Use an apostrophe in contractions.

Example: He **has not** got a chance to win the race.   *becomes*
He **hasn't** got a chance to win the race.

3. Use an apostrophe to show the plural of letters of the alphabet, abbreviations, dates, and numerals. Also, an apostrophe is needed to show numbers missing.

Examples: The children in kindergarten learned their **abc's**.
My grandfather was born in the **40's**.
The last time the Maple Leafs won the Stanley Cup was **'67**.

Exercise D

Add the missing apostrophes. Make any other changes that are necessary.

1. Form contractions

   a. was not _____
   b. I will _____
   c. will not _____
   d. he has _____
   e. did not _____
   f. it is _____
   g. can not _____
   h. is not _____
   i. I am _____
   j. do not _____

2. Shorten numbers

   a. 1962 _____
   b. 2002 _____
   c. 1995 _____

3. Make plurals

   a. 1950s _____
   b. p and q _____
   c. 5 _____

4. Change nouns to possessive form

   a. Paul _____
   b. team _____
   c. boy _____
   d. women _____
   e. Ross _____
   f. doctors _____

Quotation Marks are used to contain the exact words of a speaker. They are also used to indicate the titles of songs, plays, television programmes, newspaper and magazine articles, and other short works.

Quotation marks are used to indicate that certain words, phrases, or sentences belong to someone else or are taken out of a book.

Example: It is important to remember that "no man is an island" and therefore we should all work together.

The phrase "no man is an island" was taken from a poem by Jonne Donne, and therefore, must be recognized as an outside source by using quotations.

Exercise E

In the following sentences, add quotations where necessary and any other punctuation that is needed.

1. When are you going on holiday asked my friend, Lucy.

2. We watched Malcolm in the Middle last night on television.

3. Linda said I'll be home late tonight.

4. The teacher read an article from a magazine entitled Getting Better Marks in School.

5. My family went to see The Lion King and heard the cast sing The Lion Sleeps Tonight.

6. My father always sings his favourite song, All You Need Is Love.

7. Do you want to put on a skit in front of the class asked Antoinetta.

8. It could be titled A Day in the Life of a Grade Four Student as she suggested.

9. The Man with Two Faces is one of Joanna's favourite chapters in the Harry Potter book, *Harry Potter and the Philosopher's Stone*.

10. Lauren and Dayna sang Happy Birthday to You to their friend, Victoria, at her surprise birthday party.

13 Punctuation, Capitalization, and Abbreviations

The Semicolon

Two related independent clauses are often joined by a conjunction. They can also be joined by a semicolon if they are related in topic.

Example: The weather was awful; it rained all night long.

Notice that the topic is bad weather, and the clause following the semicolon adds information or supports the idea of the clause that goes before it.

Exercise A

Match each independent clause from Column A with a related one from Column B. Write the independent clauses connected by a semicolon in the spaces provided.

The clause following the semicolon does not begin with a capital letter.

Column A

1. The final minute of the game was exciting.
2. Paul was an excellent artist.
3. Rain poured down for most of the morning.
4. The fire alarm sounded.
5. His new bicycle was stolen.
6. The science test was scheduled for Friday.

Column B

- The ground was too soggy for a soccer game.
- The police said they would look for it.
- His paintings were hung in the hallway.
- Therefore, I studied for most of Thursday night.
- Luckily, it was only a drill.
- The score was tied.

1. _____

2. _____

3. _____

4. _____

5. _____

6. _____

The **Colon** is used to:

1. introduce a series of items.

Example: She likes to eat the following fruits: apples, peaches, pears, and plums.

2. set off a phrase that explains an idea that comes before.

Example: The school rule is as follows: students are expected to be on time.

3. set off an explanatory term (also known as an appositive).

Example: The school did fundraising for one reason only: to buy more reference books.

Insert a colon in the proper place in each sentence below.

1. Danny plays many sports basketball, tennis, soccer, and baseball.

2. The teacher has one request all pupils complete their homework.

3. He had a great idea to form a homework club.

4. You have to remember never play with matches again.

5. She invited the following friends Amanda, Olivia, Samantha, and Jessica.

6. Roger had one main goal he wanted to win the scoring title.

7. Her parents asked her to do the following empty the dishwasher, clean her room, and take out the garbage.

8. They brought their pets to school for one reason show-and-tell.

 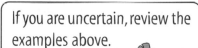

CHALLENGE

Place either a semicolon or a colon in the space provided in each sentence below.

> If you are uncertain, review the examples above.

1. He ran his best race ___ yet, he did not win.

2. The referee tossed the coin ___ we got the ball first.

3. For our family trip, we packed the following ___ clothes, food, games, and books.

4. My mom says a holiday for her would include ___ reading a good book, relaxing by the lake, and sleeping in each morning.

5. A holiday for my dad has one meaning ___ no work.

Capitalization

1. Capitalize the first word in a sentence – **It** was a beautiful day.
2. Capitalize proper nouns and adjectives including titles – **J**ohn was a **C**anadian who lived on **E**lm **S**treet. **H**e worked at the university and was called **P**rofessor **S**mith.
3. Capitalize specific places – We travelled to **B**anff, **A**lberta.
4. Capitalize days, weeks, months, holidays, and events – **R**emembrance **D**ay falls on **N**ovember 11; in the year 2001, it was on a **S**unday.
5. Capitalize the names of organizations – He played hockey in the **N**ational **H**ockey **L**eague. His father worked for the **M**unicipality, and was a member of the **R**otary **C**lub.
6. Capitalize races, nationalities, religions, and languages – My friend is a **C**atholic; he attends **S**t. **M**ary's **C**hurch. He speaks **S**panish, **E**nglish, and **F**rench.

Exercise C

With a dark pen or pencil, write over the letters that should be capitalized in each sentence. In the space following each sentence, put in the rule number that matches your correction.

1. my father doesn't get home until after supper some nights when he has to work late. _____

2. My friend and I joined the boy scouts. _____

3. My uncle works for the department of transport. _____

4. This summer, we will travel to quebec city. _____

5. Although she was french, she spoke german and italian. _____

6. We celebrate canada day each year on July 1. _____

7. The cities of montreal and quebec are on the st. lawrence river. _____

8. Every summer we go to the canadian national exhibition. _____

CHALLENGE

Circle the words in the following sentences that should not be capitalized.

There are four improper capitals.

1. The Atlantic Ocean is sometimes a very rough Ocean to cross. Many Ships have sunk in the enormous waves.
2. My cousin lives in the East, just North-east of the city of Halifax.
3. The Company my dad works for is the Ford Motor Company.

Abbreviations

In most cases it is a good idea to avoid abbreviations. However, they are acceptable in some situations.

Exercise D

Match each of the abbreviations below with the standard, expanded form of the word or phrase.

A. after noon	B. mister	C. doctor	D. inches
E. miles	F. before noon		G. number
H. road	I. United States of America		J. versus
K. for example	L. centimetres		

1. no. _____   2. a.m. _____   3. in. _____

4. p.m. _____   5. Dr. _____   6. Mr. _____

7. Rd. _____   8. e.g. _____   9. mi. _____

10. U.S.A. _____   11. vs. _____   12. cm. _____

 CHALLENGE

Here are some common abbreviations. Can you write the standard, expanded form of each abbreviation?

1. RCMP _____

2. Mt. _____

3. Jr. _____

4. Ave. _____

5. TV _____

 **Do the Challenge above ASAP. Do you know what ASAP is short for?**

Answer: 6. _____

14 Tips for Effective Writing

Complete Sentences

Always double check your sentences to make sure that they contain a subject and a verb.

Example: Incorrect – Sharon looking out the window.

This sentence lacks a verb. The word "looking" is a verbal.

Correct – Sharon **was looking** out the window.

Exercise A

For each of the following sentences, write S for subject or V for verb to indicate which is missing. Write the corrected sentence in the space provided.

> One of the sentences below is missing both a subject and verb.

1. The store owner up the shop early. _____

   _____

2. Paul across the field to get the ball. _____

   _____

3. Looked everywhere for my missing cat. _____

   _____

4. She down the street in the rain. _____

   _____

5. To earn extra money to buy a new bike. _____

   _____

Subject-Verb Agreement

In properly written sentences the subject and verb must agree in number and in person.

Example: Incorrect – There's lots of coins in the jar.

> It should be: "There are lots of coins in the jar."

Exercise B

Cross out the incorrect verb in each of the following sentences and write the correct one in the space provided.

1. Paul and Richard was best friends. _____

2. The group are arriving this afternoon.   _____

3. He always want me to show him my work.   _____

4. Bacon and eggs is his favourite meal.   _____

5. Anita and Rachel plays computer games.   _____

6. The teacher walk up and down when he teaches a lesson.   _____

7. The ballerina dance with strength and grace.   _____

8. John accidentally thrown the ball through the window.   _____

Short, Choppy Sentences

Short sentences are effective if they express an emotion. Too many short sentences, particularly when they are repetitive, can be annoying to the reader.

Example (1): Look out, there's a car coming!
(This sentence is effective because it is emphatic.)

Example (2): We played baseball. We played all afternoon.
(These two sentences should be combined to become "We played baseball all afternoon.")

Exercise C

Combine the following choppy sentences to form one sentence.

> Try not to leave out any details. Remove repeated words.

1. It was the morning. It was raining. It was raining hard.

   _____

2. The game began. The game began on time. The game began in the afternoon.

   _____

3. We had pizza. The pizza was for our lunch. The pizza was delicious. The pizza was free.

   _____

4. We stood in a line-up. The line-up was to see the first *Harry Potter* movie.

   _____

5. We ran. We jumped. We skipped. We went across the schoolyard.

   _____

Common Punctuation Errors

Here are a few common punctuation errors:

1. **Apostrophe Use**:
   a. Possessive Form: Incorrect: He borrowed Pauls bicycle.
      Correct: He borrowed Paul's bicycle.
   b. Contractions: Incorrect: We cant go out this afternoon.
      Correct: We can't go out this afternoon.

2. **Comma Use**:
   a. With items in a list: Incorrect: He wears a hat a scarf and gloves in winter.
                              Correct :   He wears a hat, a scarf, and gloves in winter.
   b. With subordinate clauses: Incorrect: We arrived, after the game was over.
                                 Correct: We arrived after the game was over.

   But, if the subordinate clause comes first in the sentence, follow it with a comma.

   Example: After the game was over, we arrived.

   c. To introduce a quotation: Incorrect: My mother asked "What time are you coming home?"
                                 Correct: My mother asked, "What time are you coming home?"

   d. Commas with dates: Incorrect: The party was scheduled for Tuesday August 6 2002.
                          Correct: The party was scheduled for Tuesday, August 6, 2002.

Exercise D

Find and correct the apostrophe and comma errors in the sentences below. Write the corrected sentences.

1. My friend said "The movie begins at two oclock."

   _____

2. We brought cookies cakes buns and pies to the bake sale.

   _____

3. I dont like trying to do things that I cant do.

   _____

4. She doesn't like waiting in line at the show to buy popcorn candy pop and ice cream.

   _____

5. Whenever we go shopping we always spend too much money.

   _____

6. I will be able to stay over at your house, if I finish cleaning my room.

   _____

Confusing Homonyms

Homonyms are words that sound the same but are spelled differently.

Examples: whole/hole, have/half, buy/by, here/hear, write/right, scene/seen, brake/break

Exercise E

In each sentence below there is a pair of homonyms to choose from. Read the sentence carefully to get its meaning, and circle the correct homonym.

1. It's / Its Jason who broke the vase.

2. We lost hour / our weigh/way in the fog.

3. Do you no / know which / witch way to go to the fare/fair?

4. We had too / two much homework on the weekend.

5. The plane / plain landed on the plane / plain.

6. If you drink the dye / die, you could die / dye.

7. My dad slammed on the car break / brake to avoid hitting the bear / bare on the highway.

8. Whose / Who's book is this?

Double Negatives

Try to avoid using more than one negative word in a sentence. Some examples of negative words are: don't, wasn't, none, no, never, no more, no one.

Some positive replacement words are: any, anyone, ever.

Example: Incorrect: He doesn't give no help to no one .

It should be: "He doesn't give any help to anyone."

Exercise F

In the sentences below, the negative words are underlined. Cross out the unnecessary negatives and change them to positive words.

1. Sheila <u>wasn't</u> <u>never</u> going to go there again.

2. Phillip <u>hasn't</u> got <u>no</u> choice but to take the school bus home.

3. He <u>didn't</u> give us <u>none</u> of the information for our project.

4. They <u>didn't</u> ask <u>nobody</u> if they <u>weren't</u> coming to the party.

5. She <u>didn't</u> tell <u>no one</u> the answer.

15 Writing Descriptive and Narrative Paragraphs

Descriptive Paragraphs

The purpose of a descriptive paragraph is to describe an action, an event, or a place. The use of vivid adjectives and adverbs will help to bring your descriptive passage to life for the reader.

Sensory Details

Sensory details appeal to our sense of smell, taste, touch, and hearing.

Exercise A

Fill in the sensory detail chart below with types of sights, sounds, and textures (things that you can feel) that might be common to the places in the chart.
Try to include at least <u>two details</u> for each place in the chart.

> At the amusement park, you might hear bells ringing as the rides start up.

Senses	Amusement Park	Restaurant	The Beach
Sight	1. 2. 3.	1. 2. 3.	1. 2. 3.
Sound	1. 2. 3.	1. 2. 3.	1. 2. 3.
Touch	1. 2. 3.	1. 2. 3.	1. 2. 3.

Writing Descriptive and Narrative Paragraphs

In Exercise A, you listed sensory details for each of the three places. Next, for each of those details, write a descriptive word.

Example: If you were describing the bells whistling at an amusement park, you could use various adjectives, such as: **loud** bells, **soft** bells, **clanging** bells.

You could compare the bells to other kinds of bells that your reader might be familiar with such as: church bells, cow bells, school bells, or fire engine bells.

You might use the word **like** to explain the type of bell ringing sound that you want to describe.

Example: When the rides were ready to go, a ring **like a church bell** rang loudly.

 Exercise B

Choose one of the topics (amusement park, beach, restaurant) from the chart in Exercise A. In the chart below, list the details from that topic. Place a descriptive word (adjective, adverb, or comparison) beside each of the details in the space provided. This will also be the topic of your paragraph writing in Exercise C.

Title: _____

Detail from your list	Description of the detail
Sight 1. _____ 2. _____ 3. _____	**Sight** 1. _____ 2. _____ 3. _____
Sound 1. _____ 2. _____ 3. _____	**Sound** 1. _____ 2. _____ 3. _____
Touch 1. _____ 2. _____ 3. _____	**Touch** 1. _____ 2. _____ 3. _____

 **Exercise C**

Write a descriptive paragraph using one of the topics from Exercise A. Refer to the details and the descriptions listed in Exercise B.

Use the plan outlined below to construct your paragraph.

Title: Use one of the titles from Exercise A or create your own.

Topic Sentence: Introduces the main idea of your paragraph; gives the reader necessary details (who, what, where, when) about your topic; leads into your descriptive sentences.

Detail Sentences: In sentence form, describe the details that you have listed in Exercise B.

Concluding Sentence: Complete your paragraph with an idea that summarizes the ideas described or the topic in general.

Title: _____

Topic Sentence: _____
_____

First Detail: _____
_____

Second Detail: _____
_____

Third Detail: _____
_____

Concluding Idea: _____
_____

 The **Narrative Paragraph** tells a story. It may use descriptive details like the descriptive paragraph, but its main purpose is the telling of a story. The story may be based on fact or may be fictitious, that is, based entirely on an imagined story. The story may be about a single event or a series of events.

Guidelines for Writing a Narrative Paragraph

1. Begin with a **topic sentence**. The topic sentence should give the reader information as to **where** or **when** your story takes place, **who** is involved in your story, and **what** your story is about.

2. When telling a story or relating an event, it is useful to place the events in the order in which they happened.

3. Use the following structure:

Beginning: Topic sentence

Middle: The sentences that give details of your story or events in the order in which they happen.

Ending (conclusion): The final sentence that offers an additional thought, a summary of the events, or something further for the reader to consider.

Write your narrative paragraph in the space below. You may choose from one of the following topics or create your own.

1.	An Embarrassing Moment	2.	Danger Was All Around Me
3.	The Summer Adventure	4.	The Worst Storm of the Winter

Title: _____

_____

_____

_____

_____

_____

_____

_____

_____

_____

_____

_____

Progress Test 2

Prepositions and Conjunctions

Complete the sentences with suitable prepositions and conjunctions.

under	with	and	of	in	over	for	or	but	until

1. After the game, we went _____ an ice cream cone _____ the mall.

2. She found her lunch box in the classroom _____ the coats.

3. Lucy and Susie _____ the grade four class are best friends.

4. I think this is the answer _____ I'm not completely sure.

5. Shane must wait _____ tomorrow to get his new bikes.

6. Beside the phone is a phone book _____ a list of all my friends' numbers.

7. You either take the money _____ leave _____ you will lose all you have.

8. The poor dog was run _____ by a truck.

Adverb or Adjective Phrases

> Only three of the phrases below are adjective phrases.

Exercise B

Identify whether each of the underlined phrases below are adjective or adverb phrases. Place "ADJ" or "ADV" in the space provided.

1. She placed her books <u>inside her school bag</u>. _____

2. The teachers <u>of our school</u> are very helpful. _____

3. <u>In the morning</u>, the paper is delivered <u>to our front door</u>. _____ _____

4. The runners raced <u>around the track</u>. _____

5. He played <u>for the local hockey team</u>. _____

6. The light <u>above the door</u> had burned out. _____

7. The boy <u>with the baseball glove</u> will pitch in the game. _____

8. I can't reach the box <u>on the top shelf</u>. _____

Dependent and Independent Clauses

Exercise C

Complete each of the following sentences with an independent (main) clause.

1. Unless the school bus comes now, _____ .

2. If we do not hurry, _____ .

3. Until we all work together, _____ .

4. Whenever we play hockey outdoors, _____ .

5. Although she was late for school every day, _____

_____ .

Exercise D

Change one of the pairs of independent clauses into a dependent clause by introducing it with a subordinating conjunction.

> Use each subordinating conjunction only once. You may have to change the order of the phrases in the sentence.

whenever	because	until
after	although	since

1. we ate dinner / we watched television

_____

2. I got a flat tire / I haven't been able to ride my bicycle

_____

3. I slept in until noon / I was still tired

_____

4. we have a picnic / it always rains

_____

5. We couldn't go to the park / we didn't have a ride

_____

6. We waited all day long / the bus arrived

_____

Progress Test 2

Complex and Compound Sentences

A complex sentence is made up of an independent clause and at least one dependent clause.
A compound sentence is made up of two independent clauses joined by a conjunction.

Exercise E

Read the following sentences. Write "complex" for complex sentences and "compound" for compound sentences.

1. While we waited for our cousins, we played Monopoly.   _____

2. The game began and we took our seats.   _____

3. Although the students practised for the play, they forgot their lines.   _____

4. We won the game because we had the better team.   _____

5. We will travel to the west coast or we will fly overseas.   _____

6. Our teacher gives lots of homework but we like doing it.   _____

7. They didn't say a word and continued to move on.   _____

Verbals

Exercise F

Underline the gerund in each of the sentences below. Indicate whether each gerund is a subject or an object by writing "subject" or "object" in the space provided.

1. Running is good exercise.   _____

2. She likes dancing to her favourite music.   _____

3. The teacher enjoys writing on the blackboard.   _____

4. Laughing is good for your health.   _____

5. Swimming in that lake is prohibited.   _____

6. Playing video games can be addictive.   _____

7. Although skiing is an expensive sport, it is worth the cost.   _____

Punctuation

Exercise G

Place the letter for the punctuation mark in the space that matches its rule of use.

Rule		Punctuation Mark
1. end of a sentence	___	A. an apostrophe
2. before and after a speech	___	B. commas
3. joins two independent clauses	___	C. a period
4. after an emphatic expression	___	D. a colon
5. follows an interrogative sentence	___	E. an exclamation mark
6. separates items in a list	___	F. a semicolon
7. comes before listing items	___	G. quotation marks
8. indicates possession	___	H. a question mark

Exercise H

In each sentence below, there are quotation marks missing. Add the necessary quotation marks and commas.

1. The grade four class memorized the poem The Vagabond Song by Bliss Carmen.

2. Scooby Doo is a very popular children's television show.

3. Shakespeare wrote the famous play Romeo and Juliet.

4. His father said Do not forget to take your house key with you.

5. What time will the movie end? she asked.

6. Gulliver's Travels is one of my favourite stories.

7. Think carefully before you make the decision the teacher reminded her.

8. One critic stated that the first Harry Potter book was a terrific read and a stunning first novel.

Exercise I

Place a semicolon or a colon in the blank space in each sentence below.

1. The morning sun melted the dew drops ___ the flowers were awakened.

2. To prepare for our trip, we purchased ___ maps, a cooler, a knapsack, and a flashlight.

3. The main idea of the story was basically ___ never be careless.

4. Sarah was the best artist in the school ___ that is, her art was always on display.

5. She couldn't go on anymore ___ she was too tired.

6. These students have to stay behind ___ Janet, Zoe, Fred, and Gord.

Exercise J

Re-write the following paragraph and add in the missing punctuation marks. Capitalize the words where necessary.

on canada day we went to ottawa for the celebration there were lots of people outside the parliament buildings although we were not able to get to the front we could get a good view of the stage the performance was superb and everyone had a good time do you want to stay for the firework display my father asked us of course we all responded excitedly

_____

_____

_____

_____

_____

_____

_____

Relative Clauses

Exercise K

Underline the relative clause in each sentence below and put "R" (restrictive) or "NR" (non-restrictive) in the space provided.

1. Her birthday, which happened to fall on February 29, was reason to celebrate. _____

2. He required the information that was needed to do the job. _____

3. The winner who was exhausted from the race stumbled forward. _____

4. The teacher, who has been on staff for many years, organized a school play. _____

5. The dog, whose name was Scamp, was a very good watchdog. _____

6. The cake, which I gave Sam for his birthday, was made by my sister. _____

7. John's father, whom everyone likes, will be our coach. _____

8. I like teachers who care. _____

Exercise L

For each pair of sentences, change one into a relative clause to form a complex sentence.

1. The room was small but tidy. We would stay there for the night.

   _____

2. I like the backpack. My mom bought it for my tenth birthday.

   _____

3. The game was boring. It lasted more than four hours.

   _____

4. The boy was funny. We called him The Joker.

   _____

5. The tall structure is the CN Tower. It stands next to the SkyDome.

   _____

Vocabulary & Usage

Seal Island

is a small rocky island about 5 km off shore in False Bay, South Africa. It is home to approximately 64,000 Cape Fur Seals.

At meal times, the seals leave the rocky area to feed on crabs, squids, and schools of fish. This becomes quite a tricky adventure during South Africa's cooler months, April to September. At this time, the fish that the Great White Shark usually <u>forages</u> on migrate to warmer waters. This leaves the seal as the main meal for these hungry <u>carnivores</u>.

Because there is a quick drop in the depth of water from the island, the sharks can move in quite close, yet be <u>camouflaged</u> by the dark, rocky bottom – a perfect <u>ambush</u> zone. The shark follows the shape of a lone or less experienced young seal swimming at the surface, waiting for the ideal time to attack.

This does sound like normal predator-prey behaviour, but what makes this one of nature's spectacular wonders is the unusual <u>breaching</u> of the Great White Shark. These sharks have been seen exploding vertically out of the water to strike and capture a seal. The <u>unsuspecting</u> seal is often sent <u>hurtling</u> into the air, which injures the seal, making it helpless and an easy meal.

This shark stalking area surrounding Seal Island has fittingly been named the "ring of peril" because the Cape Fur Seal risks its life each time it leaves the safety of its rocky hangout.

A. Use context clues to find the meaning of the underlined words in the passage. Colour the shark that has the correct meaning.

When reading an unfamiliar word, look for clues or information in the sentence to help find the meaning of the word.

1.	<u>forage</u>	feed	anger	sleep
2.	<u>carnivores</u>	animals	meat-eaters	fish
3.	<u>camouflaged</u>	tricked	attacked	hidden
4.	<u>ambush</u>	trap	home	meal
5.	<u>breaching</u>	eating	swimming	leaping
6.	<u>unsuspecting</u>	sneaky	surprised	guilty
7.	<u>hurtling</u>	catching	throwing	hopping

B. Find 4 words from the passage that start with each letter. Write them in alphabetical order.

s

m

1. _____

2. _____

_____

_____

_____

_____

_____

_____

◆ **c**   ◆ **p**

3. _____   4. _____

   _____   _____

   _____   _____

   _____   _____

Some English words come from other languages and have been changed over time. **Etymology** *is information about how and where a word originated.*

C. **Combine the Latin words below to create 3 new English words. Using the clues provided, write the meaning for each new word. List 2 animals that would be an example of each.**

> "Caro" is a Latin word meaning "flesh".
> "Herba" is a Latin word meaning "vegetation".
> "Omni" is a Latin word meaning "all".
> "Vorare" is a Latin word meaning "to swallow".

1. caro + vorare = _____

    A. omnivore   B. carnivore   C. herbivore

    Meaning: _____

    Examples: _____ and _____

2. herba + vorare = _____

    A. herbivore   B. omnivore   C. carnivore

    Meaning: _____

    Examples: _____ and _____

3. omni + vorare = _____

    A. carnivore   B. herbivore   C. omnivore

    Meaning: _____

    Examples: _____ and _____

D. Imagine that you are a journalist for a wildlife magazine. You have just visited the waters around Seal Island. Write a report with interesting details about your observations.

2 More than Candy

PEZ is a delicious fruity candy that comes with a candy holder that is available in assorted styles of heads. Eduard Haas III invented PEZ in 1927 in Vienna, Austria. It was originally sold in a peppermint flavour. The German word for peppermint is "pfefferminz". Eduard simply abbreviated the German word and came up with the now familiar word "PEZ".

In the beginning, PEZ was a breath mint for adults. The sales, however, were quite low and Haas had to come up with another plan. In 1952, he opened an office in the United States and changed his product and selling strategy. In addition to the mint flavour, he made fruit flavours in different coloured tablets, and he put character heads on the top of the dispensers. The new PEZ was a huge success with children.

Now there are over 275 different PEZ heads, ranging from Mickey Mouse to Santa Claus and Spiderman to Mary Poppins. PEZ is not just a fun treat for children – the dispensers have actually become collector items. There are even PEZ conventions held around the world, as well as a PEZ museum in California.

PEZ's popularity over the years could be due to the everchanging dispenser heads, which keep up with today's characters from cartoons, movies, and comics.

Another possible reason that PEZ has been able to maintain its popularity is the fact that toys and candy have always appealed to children.

A. **Use the definition, paragraph, and letter space clues to find the matching puzzle words from the passage.**

1. interested or attracted (Paragraph 4)

   ___ ___ ___ ___ ___ ___ ___ ___

2. a plan (Paragraph 2)

   ___ ___ ___ ___ ___ ___ ___ ___

3. different kinds (Paragraph 1)

   ___ ___ ___ ___ ___ ___ ___ ___

4. container that holds something (Paragraph 4)

   ___ ___ ___ ___ ___ ___ ___ ___ ___

5. meetings (Paragraph 3)

   ___ ___ ___ ___ ___ ___ ___ ___ ___ ___

6. in the beginning (Paragraph 1)

   ___ ___ ___ ___ ___ ___ ___ ___ ___ ___

B. **List 5 different fruit flavours that you would like to see in your favourite candy. For each flavour, write an adjective or descriptive word that starts with the same letter.**

Adjective	**Fruit Flavour**
1. _____	_____
2. _____	_____
3. _____	_____
4. _____	_____
5. _____	_____

C. PEZ is the abbreviated word for the German word of peppermint – "pffefferminz". Match the words below with their abbreviated forms. Print the letters in the boxes provided.

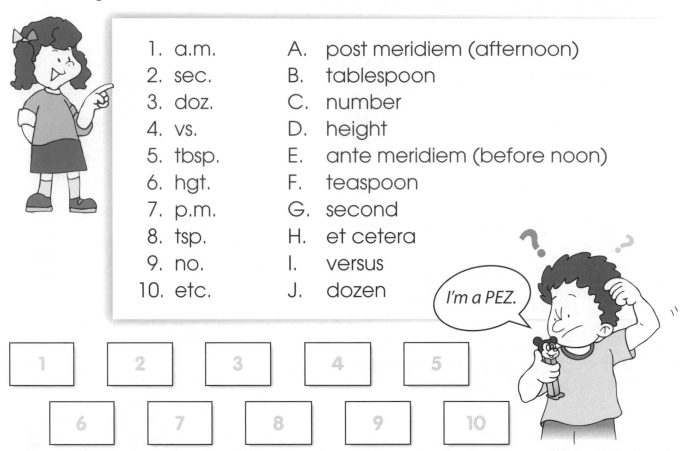

1. a.m.	A. post meridiem (afternoon)
2. sec.	B. tablespoon
3. doz.	C. number
4. vs.	D. height
5. tbsp.	E. ante meridiem (before noon)
6. hgt.	F. teaspoon
7. p.m.	G. second
8. tsp.	H. et cetera
9. no.	I. versus
10. etc.	J. dozen

I'm a PEZ.

1	2	3	4	5

6	7	8	9	10

D. PEZ dispensers are just one example of the many items that people collect. List **8** other things that are collectibles.

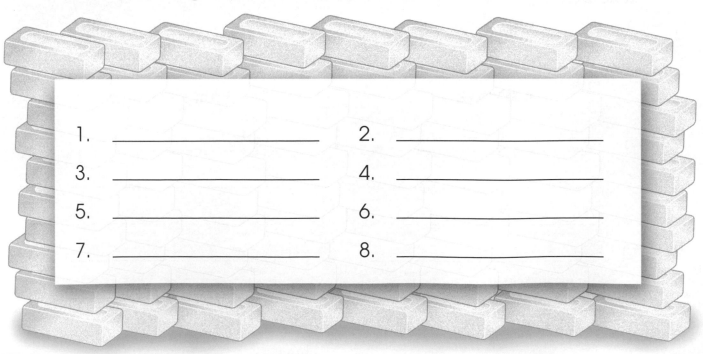

1. _____   2. _____

3. _____   4. _____

5. _____   6. _____

7. _____   8. _____

E. If you could create a candy of your choice, describe what it would be.

This may include the product name, ingredients used, how it's made, what it looks like, etc.

_____

_____

_____

F. Design an advertisement for this new product. Include a catchy title and write three great things about your candy to convince people to buy it.

Design the packaging for your new candy. Make it colourful and attractive.

3 The Surprise Holiday

David and Kim's parents were very good at organizing activities and gatherings for their family and friends. Early in the year, they started planning a surprise family vacation for their children. Flight tickets were secretly booked, hotel <u>accommodations</u> were pre-arranged, a rental car was waiting at the airport <u>destination</u>, and even the packing was done while the children were asleep!

The much-<u>anticipated</u> day had finally arrived. While David and Kim's father finished hiding the last suitcase in the back of the van, their mother was waking them up for the day. She told them that they would be going on a day's <u>excursion</u>. Perhaps they would go out for breakfast, do some shopping, and spend some time at a park. Kim and David, still feeling somewhat <u>drowsy</u>, did not question their mother about details, and proceeded to get themselves ready. Everyone piled in the van and they were off – but to where?

As they approached the highway exit to the airport, their mother took out the newly purchased video camera, focused it on the children, and began filming. While driving, their father began to reveal where they were headed. It was at this time that the confusion, <u>disbelief</u>, and finally the excitement began. Captured on film were their priceless facial expressions and reactions. Kim and David's dream was going to be a <u>reality</u>. Or was it? Over the shouts, squeals, and laughter, there was the faint sound of a siren. Oops! With all of the <u>commotion</u>, their dad hadn't realized that he was speeding.

A. Write the ending of the story.

_____

_____

_____

_____

_____

_____

_____

_____

_____

_____

_____

B. Match the words from the passage with the proper definitions. Write the representing letters only.

1. accommodations ( ) A. outing
2. destination ( ) B. being actually true
3. anticipated ( ) C. a place to stay
4. drowsy ( ) D. looked forward to
5. commotion ( ) E. the end of a journey
6. disbelief ( ) F. excitement
7. reality ( ) G. feeling that something is not true
8. excursion ( ) H. sleepy

C. Sort the words below under the correct syllable heading.

drowsy	expressions	everyone	purchased
disbelief	destination	vacation	activities
suitcase	reality	question	reactions

Two Syllables	Three Syllables	Four Syllables
_____	_____	_____
_____	_____	_____
_____	_____	_____
_____	_____	_____

D. Using a hyphen, show the different ways that these words can be divided at the end of a line.

Example: **different**   dif-ferent   differ-ent

A hyphen may be used to divide a word at a syllable break if you run out of room at the end of a line. The hyphen tells the reader to look on the next line to find the rest of the word.

1.	children	
2.	airplane	
3.	parents	
4.	hotel	
5.	beautiful	
6.	holiday	
7.	directions	
8.	happiness	

E. Use each word in an interesting sentence. Make each sentence at least 8 words long.

1. awesome _____

_____

2. silently _____

_____

3. unusual _____

_____

4. enjoyable _____

_____

5. amazement _____

_____

F. Use the number and alphabet code to find out where David and Kim really were going on their surprise holiday.

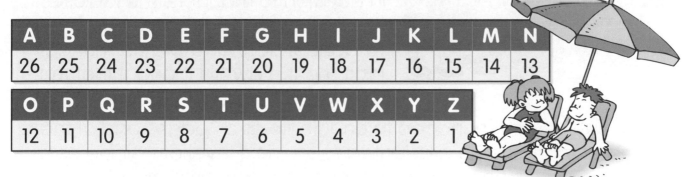

A	B	C	D	E	F	G	H	I	J	K	L	M	N
26	25	24	23	22	21	20	19	18	17	16	15	14	13

O	P	Q	R	S	T	U	V	W	X	Y	Z
12	11	10	9	8	7	6	5	4	3	2	1

15, 26, 7, 4   8, 18, 2, 23, 22, 13   9, 15, 12, 23, 4

G. Unscramble the coded words in (F).

_____   _____   _____

Edward was a fortunate boy because he was born the son of a nobleman during the Middle Ages. He knew that one day he would become a knight, just like his father. He dreamed of the knighting ceremony where he would be dubbed "Sir Edward".

Finally, the day arrived when Edward could start training to be a knight. He had mixed feelings when he was sent from his home at the age of seven to live at Lord Henry's castle. Leaving home was difficult, but he knew that it was required.

Upon arrival at the castle, the first level of training as a "page" began. Edward learned how to hunt with a falcon and handle weapons and armour. He also spent much of his time mounted on a horse and strengthening his body by wrestling. He knew that these were all skills important for a knight. Edward did not understand, however, why he needed training in manners; he felt that he was already polite enough. In addition to manners, the ladies of the castle also taught Edward how to dance, sing, and play a musical instrument. Edward thought that this was worse than being tortured.

But Edward managed to endure life as a "page" and at the age of fourteen, he graduated to the next level of training as a "squire". Fighting practice was one of his favourite exercises. He was also assigned to be the personal servant for Sir Andrew. Along with caring for this knight's weapons and armour, Edward accompanied Sir Andrew onto the battlefield. On many occasions, Edward had to assist Sir Andrew when he was knocked off his horse or wounded by an opponent's lance. He found these to be frightful experiences. However, with time Edward grew stronger and braver, and he mastered his fighting skills.

A. Use the clues below to solve the crossword puzzle. Each word answer can be found in the passage.

Across

A. lucky (para. 1)

B. seated for riding a horse (para. 3)

C. person on the opposite side in a contest (para. 4)

D. struck lightly with a sword in a knighting ceremony (para. 1)

Down

1. went along with someone or something (para. 4)

2. survive or get through a tough experience (para. 4)

3. showed expertise or great ability in a skill (para. 4)

4. long sword-like weapon (para. 4)

5. honourable man of high ranking (para. 1)

B. Each word below has the long "e" sound written as "ea", "ee", or "ie". Fill in the missing vowels on the spaces.

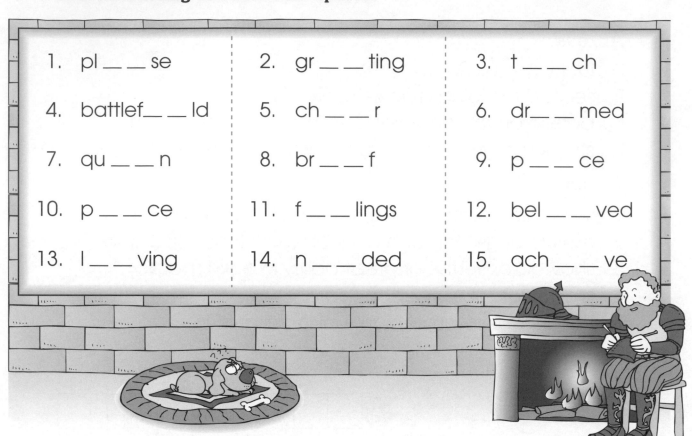

1. pl __ __ se

2. gr __ __ ting

3. t __ __ ch

4. battlef__ __ld

5. ch __ __ r

6. dr__ __ med

7. qu __ __ n

8. br __ __ f

9. p __ __ ce

10. p __ __ ce

11. f __ __ lings

12. bel __ __ ved

13. l __ __ ving

14. n __ __ ded

15. ach __ __ ve

C. Read the words in each row. Cross out the word that does not belong. Then write what the 3 words have in common.

1. lord   king   friend   knight

_____

2. fighting   teaching   educating   training

_____

3. weapon   servant   armour   shield

_____

4. joust   dance   sing   manners

_____

5. courage   strength   skill   ceremony

_____

D. Write these words under the correct heading. Number the words in each column alphabetically (from 1 to 6).

skills   lady   born   manners

level   castle   training   falcon   wrestling

experiences   lance   riding   lord

ceremony   stronger   knight   fighting   taught

"a" to "h"	"i" to "p"	"q" to "z"

E. Imagine that you are training to be a page or squire. Write a letter to your family describing your experiences and feelings.

Dear _____

_____

_____

_____

_____

_____

_____

_____

_____

5 Hear Ye... Hear Ye! (Part 2)

At the age of twenty, Edward was deemed worthy of knighthood. He had survived thirteen strict and challenging years of training with Sir Andrew. It was now the eve of becoming a knight. How could he possibly be well rested for the ceremony when there were so many rituals to perform?

As all other squires before him, Edward dressed himself in white. He spent the night in the chapel of the castle, fasting and praying, while keeping watch over his armour and weapons that were displayed on the altar. Edward could scarcely keep his eyes open and his stomach rumbled with hunger. Morning seemed like an eternity away, but then he captured a glimpse of light and realized the sun was beginning to rise. The moment that he awaited for so many years was approaching.

It was morning, and still more rituals needed to be followed before the dubbing ceremony. As a symbol of purification, Edward bathed. He was then dressed in the traditional knighting colours of red, white, and brown. The fast was finally over and Edward was permitted to eat breakfast.

The ceremony was about to begin. Edward was thrilled to see his family and friends present among the crowd. He took his oath of chivalry where he promised to defend the weak, be courteous and loyal, and follow Christianity. He then knelt before Lord Henry and bowed his head. Lord Henry tapped Edward on each shoulder with the flat of his sword and spoke the words that Edward had longed to hear, "I dub thee Sir Edward!"

A great feast followed the ceremony with food, dancing, and merriment. Edward was grateful for the years of instruction he had received, even the dancing lessons.

A. Read each underlined example from the story. On the line provided, print the letter of the matching definition.

1. ____ "the <u>eve</u> of becoming a knight"

   A. based on a belief that is passed on over years

2. ____ "so many <u>rituals</u> to perform"

   B. a religion

3. ____ "<u>fast</u> was finally over"

   C. cleansing

4. ____ "an <u>eternity</u> away"

   D. ceremonial behaviours

5. ____ "a symbol of <u>purification</u>"

   E. night before

6. ____ "<u>traditional</u> knighting colours"

   F. judged

7. ____ "<u>oath</u> of <u>chivalry</u>"

   G. not being allowed to eat

8. ____ "follow <u>Christianity</u>"

   H. quick look

9. ____ "captured a <u>glimpse</u> of light"

   I. lasting forever

10. ____ "<u>deemed</u> worthy of knighthood"

   J. promise to show the qualities expected in a knight

B. Write an acrostic poem about a knight.

The letters of the topic word are used as the beginning letter for each line in the poem. Each line of poetry must be about the writing topic.

Example:

P ractice with weapons

A lways working hard

G raduates to be a squire

E ducated in manners

K _____

N _____

I _____

G _____

H _____

T _____

C. Each word below has the long "a" sound written as "ay", "ai", or "a __ e". Fill in the missing vowels on the lines.

1. tod __ __

2. sl __ v __

3. p __ __ n

4. f __ __ th

5. s __ __ ing

6. sh __ m __

7. st __ __ ed

8. pl __ t __

9. pr __ __ se

10. aw __ __

11. tr __ __ ning

12. b __ th __ d

13. aw __ __ ted

14. gr __ t __ ful

15. displ __ __ ed

D. Use the clues to make words that begin with "kn".

> Words that begin with "kn" as in "knee" have the "n" sound; the "k" is silent.

1. kn __ __ __ __ ➤ homophone for "night"

2. kn __ __ __ ➤ rhymes with "life"

3. kn __ __ ➤ joint on the leg

4. kn __ __ __ ➤ press and fold dough into a mixture

5. kn __ __ ➤ homophone for "not"

6. kn __ __ ➤ past tense of "know"

7. kn __ __ __ __ __ ➤ rhymes with "buckle"

8. kn __ __ ➤ homophone for "no"

9. kn __ __ __ ➤ past tense of "kneel"

Challenge

kn __ __ __ __ __ __ __ ➤ learned information

Each page in a dictionary has two words at the top. They are called **guide words**. The guide word on the left is the first entry word on that dictionary page. The one on the right is the last.

E.   Circle the words that would be found on the dictionary page with each set of guide words.

decide	**demand**
defend	deem
develop	deliver
deny	determine
defeat	declare

lord	**loyal**
lookout	lovely
loser	lower
longed	loyalty
loud	lost

feast	**festival**
fear	feud
feather	feat
feed	fellow
fetch	feel

tradition	**trait**
tragic	training
trail	track
trap	travel
trade	traipse

F.   Each of these sentences has errors. Edit and rewrite the sentences so that they are correct.

1.   edward studyed many year too be come a night

_____

2.   wood you like to lived during the midle ages

_____

3.   tomorro edward was dubbed bye lord henry

_____

6 The Case of the Disappearing Fish

José lived in the suburbs near Rattray Marsh. He had a gorgeous backyard with an <u>abundance</u> of <u>foliage</u>, a variety of flowering plants, and a garden pond with a trickling waterfall. His backyard gave you the feeling of being in paradise.

The pond was José's pride and joy. He had worked <u>diligently</u> to make it a <u>suitable</u> environment for the fish and frogs that he had purchased at the <u>local</u> pet store. It was also the <u>envy</u> of the entire neighbourhood except two neighbours, Jim and Grace.

Grace was an animal lover who believed that animals should not be kept in <u>captivity</u>. She often threatened to capture José's fish and frogs and release them into a natural pond habitat. Jim, on the other hand, loved fish and frogs, especially when they were breaded and deep-fried. He often teased José about sneaking into his backyard to catch a delicious seafood meal.

One Saturday morning, José noticed that one of his fish had disappeared. The next morning, he discovered that another fish was missing. The following day, the same thing occurred. José's fish population was quickly vanishing. Someone or something was stealing them. He drew up a list of possible suspects. At the top of the list was Grace; next was Jim. He also <u>recalled</u> a <u>suspicious</u> cat walking along the fence one day. It could be the <u>culprit</u>.

José decided to stay up one night to capture the thief. He waited outside, hidden behind a bush for hours. It was sunrise and he had almost given up hope, when a large <u>swooping</u> creature came <u>skimming</u> over the top of his head. His eyes widened with disbelief. José had been completely wrong.

A. Imagine that you are a detective. Use the following clues to determine what was stealing José's fish.

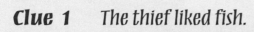

Clue 1 The thief liked fish.

Clue 2 The creature was large and could fly.

Clue 3 José lived near Rattray Marsh.

Clue 4 The creature's name rhymes with "Karen".

Answer: _____

B. Unscramble the words below and put them together to make a compound word. Each compound word can be found in the passage about José.

Compound words are 2 separate words put together to make 1 word.

1. ase+ofdo = _____
2. meos+eno = _____
3. uns+sier = _____
4. cakb+ryda = _____
5. itsu+leab = _____
6. esmo+gihnt = _____
7. retwa+lafl = _____
8. uto+dies = _____

Challenge

hribnoegu+doho = _____

Synonyms are words that have the same meaning. (happy – glad)
Antonyms are words that have opposite meaning. (happy – sad)

C. Complete the word puzzles below with the underlined words from the reading passage.

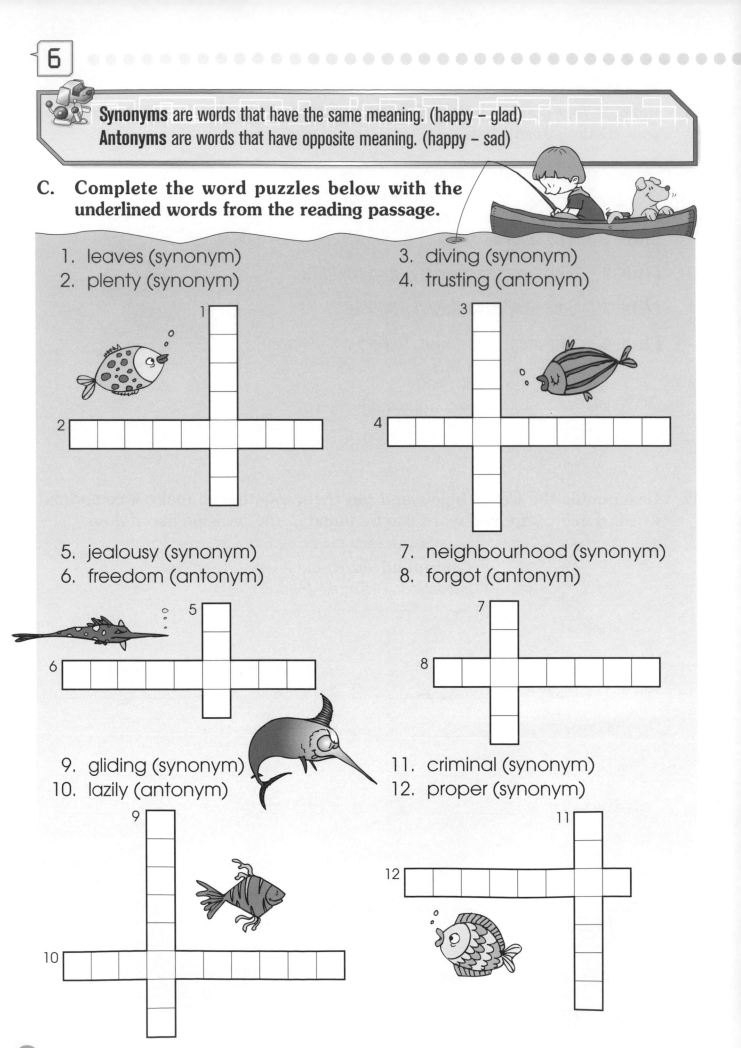

1. leaves (synonym)
2. plenty (synonym)

3. diving (synonym)
4. trusting (antonym)

5. jealousy (synonym)
6. freedom (antonym)

7. neighbourhood (synonym)
8. forgot (antonym)

9. gliding (synonym)
10. lazily (antonym)

11. criminal (synonym)
12. proper (synonym)

D. Each sentence <u>tells</u> how José feels. Rewrite each sentence using descriptive language to <u>show</u> in detail how José is feeling.

> **Examples:** tell – Grace was angry.
>
> show – Grace's face burned with rage as she stomped to José's house and pounded on the front door.

1. José was proud.

   _____

   _____

2. José was confused.

   _____

   _____

> The **setting** of a story describes the place where the story occurs. It also tells **when** the story takes place (season, time of day, past, present, or future) and the **mood** of the story.

E. Describe the setting of "The Case of the Disappearing Fish". Illustrate the setting the way you imagine it.

_____

_____

_____

_____

_____

_____

Not a Typical Grandma

My grandma is not a <u>typical</u> grandma. I don't call her Grandma because she thinks it makes her sound "over the hill". She prefers Grammy or Grams.

My grandma doesn't look like a typical grandma. Grams has long, beautiful, light-brown hair. When she's swimming or hiking, she puts her hair up in two pigtails, making her look like a Barbie doll. Grams has great fashion sense too. Her <u>wardrobe</u> is exploding with funky outfits. When it comes to <u>attire</u> for an <u>elaborate</u> occasion, she is always "dressed to the nines".

My grandma doesn't live in one place for any length of time like a typical grandma. She has "ants in her pants" because she's always <u>traversing</u> the world. She is presently living in Toronto, where she is writing a book. Last year, Grammy <u>resided</u> in Australia, where she was a student at a university. Before that, she was in South Africa, on safari adventures and climbing sand dunes in the desert.

My grandma doesn't act like a typical grandma. She loves to go rollerblading, whitewater-rafting, and mountain-climbing. Grammy also enjoys tobogganing. She doesn't watch from the top of the hill; rather she is <u>plummeting</u> down the hill at top speed on her toboggan. We go horseback-riding too. She "goes like the wind".

My grandma doesn't like to cook like a typical grandma. When we're together, I get treated to meals at my favourite restaurants and <u>delectable</u> desserts at cafés.

My grandma isn't a typical grandma, but she is a whole lot of other things; she is the "greatest thing since sliced bread".

A. Circle the most appropriate meanings for the underlined words in the passage.

1. elaborate	A. casual	B. busy	C. fancy
2. traversing	A. phoning	B. travelling	C. reading
3. plummeting	A. rising	B. bouncing	C. diving
4. typical	A. usual	B. different	C. same
5. wardrobe	A. closet	B. bedroom	C. housecoat
6. attire	A. wheel	B. hairstyle	C. clothing
7. resided	A. visited	B. lived	C. travelled
8. delectable	A. delicious	B. fattening	C. expensive

B. Use context clues from the passage to match the expressions from Column A to the meanings in Column B.

Column A

_____ 1. over the hill (para. 1)

_____ 2. dressed to the nines (para. 2)

_____ 3. ants in her pants (para. 3)

_____ 4. goes like the wind (para. 4)

_____ 5. greatest thing since sliced bread (para. 5)

Column B

A. fast

B. old

C. wonderful

D. nicely clothed

E. on the move

C. **Find four "ou" and two "ow" words from the reading passage. Write them on the lines provided.**

Words with the sound "ou" can be spelled with the letters "ou" as in "<u>out</u>" or the letters "ow" as in "<u>cow</u>".

"ou" words

1. _____   2. _____
3. _____   4. _____

"ow" words

1. _____   2. _____

D. **Write the "ou" or "ow" word that answers each clue.**

1. opposite of "inside"   __ __ __
2. homophone of "flour"   __ __ __ __ __ __
3. worn by a king or queen   __ __ __ __ __
4. opposite of "lost"   __ __ __ __ __
5. used in baking bread   __ __ __ __ __
6. opposite of "whisper"   __ __ __ __ __
7. "Mickey and Minnie..."   __ __ __ __ __
8. opposite of "sunny"   __ __ __ __ __ __
9. "The Fox and the..."   __ __ __ __ __

Challenge

When parents give their children money for helping out with chores, it is called an __ __ __ __ __ __ __ __ __ __ .

E. Write a fictional or non-fictional paragraph called "Grandma".

> *Fiction* is a made-up story. *Non-fiction* is a true story.

_____

_____

_____

_____

_____

_____

_____

F. List the similarities and differences of the grandma character from the reading passage and the grandma character in the story that you wrote.

Similarities	Differences
_____	_____
_____	_____
_____	_____
_____	_____
_____	_____

A. **Read the recipe. Fill in the boxes with the appropriate abbreviations for the underlined words.**

tsp.   avg.   C.   etc.   min.   dz.   vs.
hgt.   pkg.   lg.   F.   lb.   tbsp.   l.   ml.
sm.   no.   c.   temp.   med.   pr.

Chocolate Chip Cookies

1. $3\frac{1}{2}$ <u>cups</u> [ ] or $\frac{7}{8}$ <u>litre</u> [ ] flour

2. 1 <u>tablespoon</u> [ ] or 15 <u>millilitres</u> [ ] baking soda

3. 1 <u>teaspoon</u> [ ] or 5 <u>millilitres</u> [ ] salt

4. $\frac{1}{2}$ <u>cup</u> [ ] or 125 <u>millilitres</u> [ ] shortening

5. $\frac{1}{2}$ <u>cup</u> [ ] or 125 <u>millilitres</u> [ ] margarine

6. 1 <u>cup</u> [ ] or 250 <u>millilitres</u> [ ] brown sugar

7. 1 <u>tablespoon</u> [ ] or 15 <u>millilitres</u> [ ] milk

8. 1 egg

9. 1 <u>large</u> [ ] <u>package</u> [ ] chocolate chips

10. Preheat oven to the <u>temperature</u> [ ] of 350° <u>Fahrenheit</u> [ ] or 175° <u>Celsius</u> [ ] . Cream shortening and sugar. Add egg and milk. Add flour, baking soda, and salt . Stir in chocolate chips. Bake for 12 <u>minutes</u> [ ] . Makes or yields 5 <u>dozen</u> [ ] <u>large</u> [ ] or 10 <u>dozen</u> [ ] <u>medium</u> [ ] cookies. Enjoy!

B. **Sort the words below under the correct syllable heading.**

delicious   measure   temperature   mixture
appetizer   preheat   tablespoon   margarine
ingredient   appetite   flavour   decoration

Two Syllables	Three Syllables	Four Syllables
_____	_____	_____
_____	_____	_____
_____	_____	_____
_____	_____	_____

C. **Read the numbered words below. Find the synonym for each in the word box.**

neighbourhood   delicious   clothing
meat-eater   different   judge   feed
forever   meetings   diving
plenty   interested   cleanse
lived   jealous   mastery

1. carnivore   _____
2. envious   _____
3. appealed   _____
4. local   _____
5. conventions   _____
6. deem   _____
7. expertise   _____
8. attire   _____
9. delectable   _____
10. resided   _____
11. purify   _____
12. eternally   _____
13. abundance   _____
14. forage   _____
15. swooping   _____
16. assorted   _____

D. Write these words under the correct heading.
Number the words in each column alphabetically
(from 1 to 6).

grill	recipe	muffins	apron	nuts
tasty	utensil	eggs	kitchen	sprinkles
pastry	serving	dessert	icing	cupcake
	chef	oven	snack	

"a" to "h"	"i" to "p"	"q" to "z"
_____	_____	_____
_____	_____	_____
_____	_____	_____
_____	_____	_____
_____	_____	_____
_____	_____	_____

E. Using a hyphen, show the different ways that these
words can be divided at the end of a line.

1. donuts   _____
2. raisins   _____
3. caramel   _____   _____
4. cinnamon   _____   _____
5. chocolate   _____   _____
6. decorate   _____   _____
7. temperature   _____   _____

          _____

F. Draw lines to match the words from Column A to the words in Column B to make compound words. Write the compound words on the lines provided.

	Column A	Column B	Compound Words
1.	dish	melon	dishwasher
2.	blue	scotch	
3.	clean	holder	
4.	water	spoon	
5.	butter	fruit	
6.	tea	berry	
7.	pot	washer	
8.	grape	up	

G. Circle the words that would be found on the dictionary page with each set of guide words.

bagel	banana
baker	ball
baste	balance
batter	basket
bacteria	barbecue

chef	chop
chill	chunky
chestnut	chip
cherry	chocolate
cheese	charcoal

flaky	flour
flatten	flavour
fluid	flipper
fluff	flatware
fresh	flapjack

special	spray
spoon	spread
spice	split
sprinkle	spatula
sponge	spend

H. Read each sentence. Write "T" if it is a "telling sentence" or "S" if it is a "showing sentence".

1. _____ I forgot to put the timer on the oven and the cookies burned.

2. _____ The kitchen was bursting with the sweet aroma of freshly baked blueberry muffins.

3. _____ We had to wait for the cookies to cool down before we could eat them.

4. _____ Every Saturday morning, I help my mother mix the ingredients for homemade bread.

5. _____ The sweetness of the melting chocolate chips made my teeth ache and my mouth water.

6. _____ The smell and sound of sizzling bacon made my stomach rumble loudly with hunger.

I. Circle the word that is the antonym for the word in each box on the left.

1. fortunate	A. excited	B. unlucky	C. nervous
2. drowsy	A. tired	B. sad	C. awake
3. peril	A. safety	B. danger	C. beautiful
4. recalled	A. spoke	B. wished	C. forgot
5. diligently	A. happily	B. lazily	C. perfectly
6. suspicious	A. trusting	B. guilty	C. nasty
7. captivity	A. caught	B. freedom	C. prison

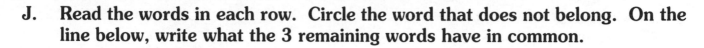

J. Read the words in each row. Circle the word that does not belong. On the line below, write what the 3 remaining words have in common.

1. knife   plate   spoon   fork

_____

2. sugar   flour   cake   baking soda

_____

3. vanilla   icing   candles   sprinkles

_____

4. pizza   cake   yogurt   cookies

_____

5. oatmeal   chocolate chip   brownies   peanut butter

_____

K. Fill in the missing vowels in each of the words below.

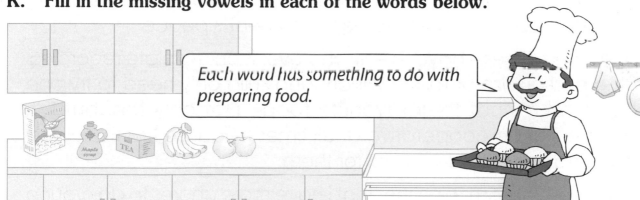

Each word has something to do with preparing food.

long "a" sound	long "e" sound	"ow" sound
spr ___ ___	gr ___ ___ se	fl ___ ___ r
gr ___ ___ n	p ___ ___ ce	paper t___ ___ el
t ___ st ___	cr ___ ___ m	gr ___ ___ nd
tr ___ ___	y ___ ___ ld	br ___ ___ n
sc ___ l ___	p ___ ___ l	p ___ ___ nd

February 1, 2004

Dear Kids Advice Magazine:

Hi, my name is Evan and being the eldest child in the family surely has its disadvantages. First of all, I have to share all my toys and games with my younger siblings, William and Julia. Of course, they don't need to return the favour because I'm totally uninterested in their things. Besides that, Julia and William are always hanging around me. It's especially irritating when I have a friend over. We look for a secluded place in the house where they can't disturb us, but within minutes, they've found us and are asking to join in. I just can't seem to get a moment's peace.

At meal times, I have to eat whatever is on my <u>plate</u> regardless of the portion size or taste. William and Julia only need to try one bite when it's not their favourite food. Not only this, but I'm expected to be cooperative at all times because I'm the oldest and need to be a role model for them.

It doesn't seem <u>fair</u> either that I have more chores to do around the house than Julia and William put together. Plus, when it comes to practising our musical <u>instruments</u>, I have to practise more than double the time. Oh, and the worst part of it all is the huge quantities of homework I get compared to them.

I'm feeling rather annoyed with my sibling situation. Can you please write back with some advice?

Yours truly,

Evan Smith

A. Imagine that you are a writer for "Kids Advice Magazine". Write a "friendly letter" back to Evan that will make him feel better. Try to sound understanding and list at least 3 advantages of being the eldest child in the family.

A *friendly letter* has 5 parts: date, greeting, body, closing, and signature.

_____
Date

_____
Greeting

Body _____

_____

_____

_____

_____

_____

_____

_____

_____
Closing

_____
Signature

B. Find the matching puzzle words from Evan's letter.

1. a quiet place away from people (paragraph 1)

   ___ ___ ___ ___ ___ ___ ___

2. the amount of something (paragraph 3)

   ___ ___ ___ ___ ___ ___ ___ ___ ___

3. brothers or sisters (paragraph 1)

   ___ ___ ___ ___ ___ ___ ___ ___

4. someone worthy of following his/her actions (paragraph 2)

   ___ ___ ___ ___   ___ ___ ___ ___ ___

Entry words are words listed in a dictionary. They are in alphabetical order and are typed in **bold**. Most words have more than one meaning.

C. Read the entry words below. Choose the correct meaning for each underlined word in Evan's letter. Write the number.

plate (plāt), n. 1. thin flat piece of metal. *The nameplate was on the trophy.* 2. home base in baseball. *The runner crossed home plate.* 3. food and service for one person. *The restaurant charged $10 a plate.* 4. shallow, circular dish that food is served on. *There were four plates on the table.* 5. firm substance that artificial teeth are attached to. *The denture plate was custom-fit to the mouth.*

1

instrument (in'strə mənt), n. 1. tool or utensil. *The instrument used in cutting is a knife.* 2. person used by another for a plan. *He was an instrument in the bank robbery.* 3. measuring device. *The speedometer is an instrument used in vehicles.* 4. legal document. *All members signed the instrument.* 5. device used to produce musical sounds. *My favourite instrument is the violin.*

2

fair (fâr), adj. 1. light in colour. *She has fair skin.* 2. following the rules. *It was a fair contest.* 3. not playing favouritism. *The teacher is fair with all students.* 4. not cloudy. *We had fair weather today.* 5. not excellent and not poor. *He is in fair health.*

3

D. **The following are some words from Evan's letter. Write the base word beside each.**

A **base word** is the word from which other words can be built by adding a prefix (beginning) and/or suffix (ending).

Example: "Believe" is the base word for "unbelievable".

1. disadvantages _____
2. younger _____
3. uninterested _____
4. totally _____
5. irritating _____
6. regardless _____
7. practising _____
8. quantities _____

E. **The paragraph below is written in the present tense. Rewrite the paragraph so that it is in the past tense.**

Evan loves to climb in the attic where he has a secret hideaway. He keeps his favourite toys and books up there. Evan is also storing Christmas presents for his family in the attic. He makes sure nobody follows him when he escapes to his hideout.

_____

_____

_____

_____

9 The Victory of Lance Armstrong

Lance Armstrong, a world champion cyclist, was already a professional triathlete at the age of 16, participating in courses of long-distance swims, bike rides, and runs.

In his senior high school years, Lance decided to focus on cycling. Within a few years, he was a member of the 1992 U.S. Olympic Team. Over the next few years, he went on to win <u>numerous</u> cycling races worldwide.

In October 1996, shortly after competing in his second Olympic Games, Lance was faced with <u>devastating</u> news. Medical tests showed that he had advanced stages of <u>cancer</u>. Medical experts <u>predicted</u> only a 40% chance of survival. With two surgeries planned, including a brain surgery, and a series of treatments, Lance was unsure if he would ever ride a bicycle again. Fortunately, the treatments and surgeries were <u>remarkably</u> successful. In February 1997, the doctors announced that Lance was a healthy man again.

Just 5 months after the <u>diagnosis</u> of cancer, Armstrong was back doing what he loved – cycling. He began a strict training schedule with hopes of a comeback. His goal was to compete in the 1999 Tour de France, which is considered the world's toughest bicycle race – a <u>gruelling</u> 23-day cycling contest through the mountains and plains of France.

Lance went on to win the Tour de France 5 years in a row. This is considered one of the greatest accomplishments in sports history. His <u>victories</u> are not just about cycling races, but winning at life itself. Lance's determination, courage, and strength <u>enabled</u> him to <u>overcome</u> the odds.

A. Use context clues to match the underlined words from the passage with the proper definitions. Write the corresponding letters.

_____ 1. numerous   A. very tiring

_____ 2. devastating   B. told ahead of time

_____ 3. cancer   C. winnings

_____ 4. predicted   D. many

_____ 5. remarkably   E. life-threatening disease

_____ 6. diagnosis   F. beat

_____ 7. gruelling   G. especially

_____ 8. victories   H. made possible

_____ 9. enabled   I. results of medical tests

_____ 10. overcome   J. terrible

B. You have been chosen to interview Lance Armstrong. He has time to answer 6 questions. Use "How" and the "5 W's of Writing" to form your well thought-out questions.

1. How _____

2. Who _____

3. What _____

4. Where _____

5. When _____

6. Why _____

Prefix Chart

A **prefix** is a syllable at the beginning of a base word that makes a new word and meaning.

Prefix	Meaning	Prefix	Meaning
tri	three	mid	middle
bi	two	dis	opposite
un	not	pre	before
re	again	mis	wrong

C. Fill in the blanks with words from the word bank. Use the prefix chart as a guide to write the meaning of each underlined word.

> uncertain   prejudged   triathlete
> misread   dismounted

1. The _____ competed in the swim, bike, and run events.

   Meaning : _____

2. The athlete _____ the rules and was disqualified from the race for going out of the pylon area too soon.

   Meaning : _____

3. It was _____ who would win the gold medal until the final lap of the course.

   Meaning : _____

4. He _____ his bicycle to give his weary legs a rest.

   Meaning : _____

5. Even after Lance had recovered from cancer, many people _____ him and thought that he would never be a successful rider again.

   Meaning : _____

Simile

A **simile** compares two different things, using the word "like" or "as". Use of similes can make writing clearer and more interesting for the reader.

Example: I dive and swim in the water **like a playful dolphin**.

D. Read the sentences and look for similes. On the lines below, write the two things that are being compared.

1. Lance rode his bike past the crowd like a bolt of lightning.

   _____ is compared to _____ .

2. Riding all day in the sun, the cyclist was as hot as sizzling bacon.

   _____ is compared to _____ .

3. His mouth was dry like the desert sand.

   _____ is compared to _____ .

E. Finish these sentences using descriptive and expressive similes.

1. Pedalling up the steep mountain, his legs felt as weak as _____
   _____

2. As he neared the finish line, his heart was pounding like _____
   _____

3. The cheering crowds echoed in his ears like _____
   _____

4. Winning the race, he felt as proud as _____
   _____

10 A Rebus Invitation

A. Read the rebus invitation. Rewrite the invitation below without using rebus.

Rebus uses a combination of letters, symbols, pictures, and words to represent a word or phrase.

Helpful Hints:

Plus (+) sign means add the picture and letter(s) together to make a word.

Example: pop + 🌽 = popcorn

A dark capital letter should be pronounced as it is in the alphabet.

Example: dAZ = daisy

~ Invitation Card ~

D + 👂 St + 🂡 + **E**,

U R inv + 👁 + ted to m + 👁 birthd**A** par + 🫖 on 🌞 + d**A**, Jul + 👁 1st. It ⭐ + ts at 2 o' + ⏰ and **N**ds at 5 o' + ⏰. We will m + 🍔 at the ☸ + er 🐴 F + 💪 on 👸 S + 🌳 + t.

Lunch will be hot + 🐕 + s, fr**N**ch fr + 👁 + s, and ☕ + 🍰 + s.

Please b + 💍 🌞 + screen and 🐝 spr**A**.

Y + 🏓 frNd,

🐚 + **E**

_____

_____

_____

_____

_____

_____

_____

_____

B. **Use pictures and symbols to make each sentence into a rebus sentence.**

1. Would you like to race with your horse?

2. Can you wait for me at the top of the mountain?

3. The rain finally stopped and the sun began to shine.

10

C. Use each of the 5 senses to describe an item from what you imagine to be the perfect birthday party.

> Here are some ideas to write about: party location, decorations, cake, activities or games, people, food and drinks, music, and presents received.

sight	
sound	
smell	
taste	
touch	

D. Using the ideas, write a paragraph that will describe this birthday party in such detail that it "paints a picture" in the reader's mind.

E. Use the chart below to answer each clue for the word search. Print the new word in the box.

A **suffix** is a word part placed at the end of a base word that makes a new word and meaning.

Suffix	Meaning	Suffix	Meaning
ful	full of	less	without
ed	in the past	ing	in the present
able	able to do	ness	state of being
ly	in a manner of	er, or	one who

In some words, you may need to change the end of the word first before adding the suffix.

Example: in a sleepy manner – **sleepily**

1. state of being happy

2. one who bakes

3. present tense of dance

4. without thanks

5. able to excite

6. full of wishes

7. one who decorates

8. without fear

9. in a usual manner

10. able to teach

11. past tense of climb

12. full of flavour

11 A Sporty Gal

Laura is an incredible athlete who would be involved in every extra-curricular activity year round if she could have her way. However, her parents view it differently. As it is, Laura's parents do an amazing juggling act of schedules to drop off and pick up Laura at practice and game locations.

During the fall, Laura runs every day on her lunch hour or after school, training for cross-country meets where she races a distance of over 1 kilometre. Following the cross-country season comes volleyball, where Laura is the "setter", considered the most important position on the court.

Right after Christmas holidays, Laura gets in shape for the basketball season. She plays the position of guard, which means she is awesome at dribbling the ball.

As soon as spring arrives comes the badminton team. Laura plays singles or doubles, where she tries to strategically shoot the "birdie" on the opponent's side where it is unreachable.

Finally, near the end of the school year is the track and field season. Laura has great upper body strength and excels at shot put. She also succeeds in high jump, where she does the "Fosbury Flop" technique.

Laura's all-star soccer team kicks in just before summer begins. She plays a defense position, responsible for protecting her team's end of the field so that the other team doesn't score.

As a result of Laura's jammed packed athletic life, she does not have much free time. This sporty gal doesn't seem to mind though, because she is crazy about sports.

Transition words help to tie ideas together. They can:

1. show the sequence of events: first, finally, before, after...
2. describe the order things are located: near, over, between...
3. add information: for instance, besides, for example...
4. compare and contrast things: similarly, although, however...
5. summarize or conclude: as a result, therefore, finally...

A. Find at least 6 transition words or phrases from the passage.

Transition words

1. _____
2. _____
3. _____
4. _____
5. _____
6. _____

B. Read the steps for how to dive in deep water. Write these steps in a paragraph using as many transition words as possible from the word box.

The first sentence is done for you. You may use the same transition word more than once.

first	once	then	finally	last
after	second	as soon as	third	next

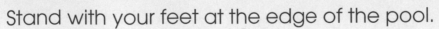

Stand with your feet at the edge of the pool.

Place one knee on the ground.

Stretch your arms over your head together.

Bend forward at the waist.

Tuck your chin.

Push off with your back foot.

Order of entry in the water is hands, head, and feet.

Once you know how to swim in deep water, you can learn how to dive. _____

_____

_____

_____

_____

_____

_____

C. **Read the following sport riddles. Answer each riddle on the line provided.**

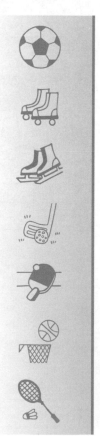

1. Five players per team on the court
   For this very exciting sport.
   They use a ball that is round,
   And into a net it is bound.
   Two points for that shot.
   A foul it is not.

   What am I? _____

2. The first one held in Greece.
   White on the flag symbolizing peace.
   Every four years are the games.
   Athletes from countries of all names.
   Summer and winter it matters not.
   The torch is lit and medals are sought.

   What am I? _____

D. Think of 5 rhyming words for each of the words listed.

> Rhyming words do not have to be spelled with the same ending or have the same number of syllables, but they must have the same ending sound.
> Example: _glide_ – rep_lied_

score	kick	speed	goal

E. Write a rhyming riddle with 3 rhyming couplets for a sport of your choice. Have a friend try to solve the riddle.

> A couplet is a 2-line verse that rhymes.

Imagine standing in the middle of a cornfield listening to a rumbling sound beneath your feet. Then to your fear and astonishment, you see the ground crack open and bulge to about 2 metres high. Smoke and ash begin to spew into the air, followed by a loud, whistling sound. This unbelievable occurrence was actually witnessed by an Indian farmer in 1943, in a Mexican village called San Salvador Paricutín.

The farmer, fearing the worst, fled the scene and returned the following morning to find that this swelling of the earth had grown to a height of 9 metres and was forcefully flinging out rocks. By the end of the same day, it grew another 36 metres. It was the birth of a volcano. Throughout the night, lava shot up over 300 metres and spread rapidly over the farmer's cornfields.

This powerful explosive period continued for a year where the cone of the volcano reached a height of 336 metres. The cone continued to grow at a slower rate for 8 more years, totalling 410 metres. Six months before the volcano died, it had its most violent activity. By the end, over 900 million tonnes of lava had destroyed San Salvador Paricutín and the neighbouring village of San Juan and volcanic ash had choked surrounding forests. Remarkably, nobody was killed by the lava or ash.

Only one building out of the two villages survived this monstrous volcano and did not get swallowed up by the lava. Still today, surrounded by hardened lava, one can see the remains of a church in the village of San Juan.

Although this volcano caused great devastation to the land of the two Mexican villages, geologists had an opportunity to observe and study this volcano from its birth until its death. It was appropriately named Paricutín, after the village where it originated.

A. Each word below has the long "o" sound, written as "ow"(gr<u>ow</u>n), "ou" (y<u>ou</u>r), "oa"(m<u>oa</u>n), or "o__e"(sm<u>o</u>ke). Fill in the missing vowels to complete the words.

1. ph __ n __	2. afl __ __ t	3. overfl __ __
4. s __ __ l	5. thr __ __	6. th __ __ gh
7. bulld __ z __	8. cl __ s __	9. gr __ __ n
10. shad __ __	11. rainc __ __ t	12. d __ __ gh

B. Select words from the word box to match with the descriptions. Write the words on the lines provided.

A word ending in the suffix "**ist**" usually indicates a person who is an expert, or one who works or studies in a certain area. For example, an "art**ist**" is someone who works in the area of art.

florist
geologist
pharmacist
pianist
scientist
machinist
dentist
violinist

1. one who performs on the piano _____

2. one who operates machinery _____

3. one who is an expert in science _____

4. one who is an expert on rocks _____

5. one who performs on the violin _____

6. one who works with flowers _____

7. one who works in the area of dental health _____

8. one who prepares medical prescriptions _____

C. Read the first paragraph of the story. Find 3 words that use onomatopoeia.

> **Onomatopoeia** *is a word that sounds like the thing that it describes.*
> **Example:** *The bee* **buzzed** *in my ear.*

1. _____   2. _____   3. _____

D. Draw lines to match each of the following phrases with the onomatopoeia that describes it.

1. old windows on a windy day •   • splash
2. eating potato chips •   • clang
3. eating spaghetti •   • crunch
4. jumping in a pool •   • bark
5. washing dishes •   • slurp
6. sound of a dog •   • rattle

E. Write a Word Cinquain Poem about volcanoes. Draw a picture to go with your cinquain.

> Follow these steps in writing your poem.
> **1st line** – 1 word – title or topic
> **2nd line** – 2 words – describing words about the topic
> **3rd line** – 3 words – actions words about the topic
> **4th line** – 4 words – feelings about the title
> **5th line** – 1 word – synonym for the title

_____

_____

_____

_____

F.

F. Read the two entries and the pronunciation symbols for each set of homographs. Then read each sentence below. Match the sentence with the numbered entry. Write the corresponding letter.

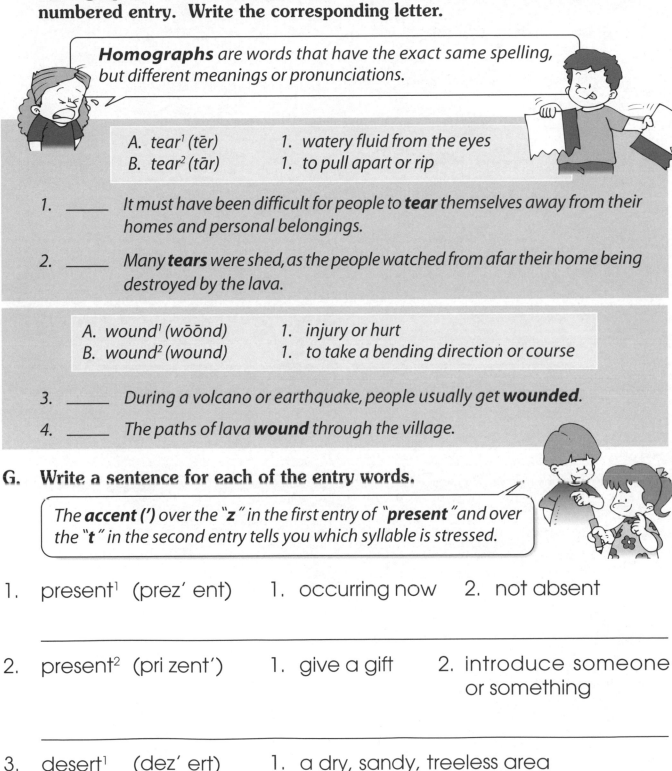

Homographs are words that have the exact same spelling, but different meanings or pronunciations.

A. tear¹ (tēr)   1. watery fluid from the eyes
B. tear² (tār)   1. to pull apart or rip

1. _____ It must have been difficult for people to **tear** themselves away from their homes and personal belongings.

2. _____ Many **tears** were shed, as the people watched from afar their home being destroyed by the lava.

A. wound¹ (wōōnd)   1. injury or hurt
B. wound² (wound)   1. to take a bending direction or course

3. _____ During a volcano or earthquake, people usually get **wounded**.

4. _____ The paths of lava **wound** through the village.

G. Write a sentence for each of the entry words.

*The **accent (')** over the "**z**" in the first entry of "**present**" and over the "**t**" in the second entry tells you which syllable is stressed.*

1. present¹ (prez' ent)   1. occurring now   2. not absent

_____

2. present² (pri zent')   1. give a gift   2. introduce someone or something

_____

3. desert¹ (dez' ert)   1. a dry, sandy, treeless area

_____

4. desert¹ (di zûrt')   1. to leave or run away

_____

13 Nature's Fireworks

For thousands of years, the Northern Lights, or in scientific terms, the Aurora borealis, have both amazed and frightened people with the eerie glow that they emit in the sky.

"Aurora borealis" is Latin (the ancient language of the Romans) and means "dawn of the North". The lights are called this because they are seen in the Northern Hemisphere. There is also a version of it in the Southern Hemisphere called the "Aurora australis". These northern and southern auroras usually appear as mirror-like images at the same time in many shapes and vivid colours.

Auroras are caused by particles that are shot out into space by the sun. When these particles reach Earth, they are drawn into the magnetic field that surrounds our planet. When these particles collide with different gases in our atmosphere, the Northern Lights are produced. Since the magnetic field is strongest in the North, that's where you can witness this marvel.

While science gives us the true reason for the Northern Lights, the myths and legends that our ancestors used to explain them are interesting. For instance, the Inuit of Alaska believed that the lights were the spirits of the animals they hunted – the seals, salmon, deer, and beluga whales. The Menominee Indians of Wisconsin regarded the lights as torches used by great, friendly giants in the North to help them spear fish at night. Other aboriginal peoples believed that the lights were the spirits of their people and some an omen of war.

If you ever get to travel to the North, grab some popcorn, settle in a lawn chair, and get ready to watch the best firework show on Earth.

A. Use context clues to determine the meaning of each underlined word in the passage. Then look up the word and write the dictionary definition.

1. **eerie**

   My definition: _____

   Dictionary definition: _____

2. **emit**

   My definition: _____

   Dictionary definition: _____

3. **ancient**

   My definition: _____

   Dictionary definition: _____

4. **vivid**

   My definition: _____

   Dictionary definition: _____

5. **particles**

   My definition: _____

   Dictionary definition: _____

6. **marvel**

   My definition: _____

   Dictionary definition: _____

7. **omen**

   My definition: _____

   Dictionary definition: _____

Persuasive writing gives an opinion and tries to convince the reader to agree with that opinion by using facts and examples.

B. Imagine that you are a journalist for a tourist magazine. Write a "persuasive" article convincing tourists to travel to the North to see the Northern Lights.

_____

_____

_____

_____

_____

_____

_____

The main idea of a paragraph is usually the first sentence of the paragraph and it is called the **topic sentence**.

C. Write your own topic sentence for the paragraph below.

_____

_____

The Northern Lights can be seen as shades of red, blue, green, yellow, and violet. The most common colours, however, are pale green and pink. They can appear looking like scattered clouds of light or wavy curtains, streamers, arcs, or shooting rays. These colourful forms of light send a beautiful glow throughout the northern night skies.

A paragraph should contain details that fit the topic sentence. These are called **supportive sentences**.

D. Read the topic sentence. Circle the letters of 3 sentences that support the main idea or topic.

> Researchers have discovered that auroral activity runs on a cycle and is best viewed at certain times.

A. The "Aurora borealis" peaks or is most visible every 11 years.

B. The last peak period was in 2002.

C. The different colours seen come from air molecules, like oxygen.

D. Winter in the North around midnight seems to elicit the best light displays.

E. Select a topic. Write a topic sentence and 3 supportive sentences that provide details about the main idea.

_____

_____

_____

_____

_____

_____

Pet Store

I heard them plead and beg for a pet of their own.
   A promise of love and care when it was brought home.
Fish, bird, cat, or rabbit would suffice.
But having a puppy would be really nice.

The pet store was full of pets to adopt.
   I was the lucky one that day, I thought.
Cuddled in her arms, freed from that store.
Onto new adventures and much, much more.
Romping in the backyard, chewing a bone.
Life was marvellous, I no longer felt alone.

But then after months, it seemed nobody cared.
   The responsibility and commitment was not shared.
The girl got busy with friends and homework, you see.
And I was stuck in a cage again, and wanted to be free.

One day I heard the mom argue with her daughter.
   Constant reminding of my walk, food, and water.
She said I'd have to be sent to another owner.
Someone not so busy; I wouldn't have to be a loner.
My happiness there was coming to an end.
How would my broken heart ever mend?

But call it a miracle or fortune, it matters not.
   It was a wonderful home where I was brought.
The lady was retired and lived on her own.
She longed for a companion; didn't want to be alone.
We were an instant match for one another.
The good times we had - like child and mother.
You'd think I was royalty - always treated like a queen.
Our affection for each other was always seen.

But sometimes I think of the girl from long ago.
   Is she grown, doing well; I'd like to know.
I have no regrets from that time, you see.
She did love me; it just wasn't meant to be.

A **stanza** is a group of lines in a poem that has rhythm and a theme. Each stanza is separated from others by a blank space on the page. It is much like a paragraph in a writing passage.

The **tone** is the writer's opinion, attitude, or feeling about the topic. It can be happy, sad, humorous, angry, etc.

A. **What is the writer's tone in each stanza of "A Pet's Tale"? Write the corresponding letter.**

_____ 1st Stanza

_____ 2nd Stanza

_____ 3rd Stanza

_____ 4th Stanza

_____ 5th Stanza

_____ 6th Stanza

A. disappointed

B. serious

C. persuasive

D. happy

E. excited

F. sad

Challenge

Who is telling the poem "A Pet's Tale"? _____

B. **Give an example of each of the following. Using these words, write a paragraph that has a "silly tone".**

A **noun** names a person, place, or thing.   (boy, city, dog)
An **adjective** describes something or somebody.   (furry)
A **verb** is an action word.   (jumped)
An **adverb** tells how something is done.   (quickly)

A name   _____

A place   _____

A verb   _____

A type of animal   _____

An adjective   _____

An adverb   _____

_____

_____

_____

_____

_____

_____

_____

_____

Some poets use **alliteration** to make their poems more interesting, humorous, or pleasing to the ear. Alliteration occurs where 2 or more words in a group of words begin with the same letter. They're also known as **tongue twisters**.

C. **Fill in the blanks with words that begin with the same letter of the alphabet.**

1. alphabet letter _____
2. name _____
3. noun _____
4. adjective _____
5. verb _____
6. adverb _____

 Challenge

Using the words above and smaller words if needed, write an alliterative sentence.

Example: Sammy the snake slithered slowly down the slippery slope.

_____

Homophones are words that sound exactly the same, but have different meanings and spellings.

Example: tail – tale

D. Circle the word that matches the picture above it.

1.

sale   sail

2.

dear   deer

3.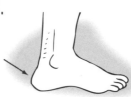

plain   plane

4.

heel   heal

5.

bear   bare

6.

rain   reign

7.

pair   pear

8.

flour   flower

E. Fill in the blanks with the correct homophones.

1. _____ pet was lost somewhere over _____ . (there, their)

2. She _____ her bike down the _____ to the farm. (rode, road)

3. The naughty dog dug one _____ after another, making our _____ backyard a mess. (hole, whole)

4. That _____ does not have grey _____ ; it has grey fur. (hair, hare)

5. I _____ the ball _____ the window by accident. (through, threw)

6. When I _____ a letter, I use my _____ hand. (right, write)

15 Camp Wannastay

Camp Wannastay

Friday July 10th

Saying good-bye to Mom, Dad, and Erica was a breeze. I imagined a whole week without my little sister <u>pestering</u> me would be like heaven, but now, I'm feeling differently. It's the end of my first day at camp and I'm <u>dreading</u> the remainder of the week. I thought I was ready for overnight camp, but I suppose I was mistaken.

Saturday July 11th

Today, camp went a lot better than I <u>anticipated</u>. Steve, the camp counsellor, is absolutely the coolest. He organized cooperative games so the campers could get acquainted with one another. We also went canoeing and I was paired up with a quiet guy named Shawn. I <u>initiated</u> conversation with him and he became more at ease. Canoeing was a blast. I think we frightened away all the wildlife with the <u>ruckus</u> we created during the splash fight with our paddles. I got totally drenched.

Sunday July 12th

Today was a great bonding experience for the guys in our cabin. The counsellor arranged a competition among the cabins. We came in fourth place in the scavenger hunt, narrowly missing third. The lake water was frigid for the swimming relay, but we placed second regardless. The final event worth the most points was the obstacle course. It was quite challenging, but an awesome time. We put forth our finest effort and it paid off – first place for our team. I can honestly say, the feeling of homesick has completely <u>diminished</u>.

A. **Match each underlined word in the journal with its meaning. Write the corresponding letter.**

1. pestering _____
2. dreading _____
3. anticipated _____
4. initiated _____
5. ruckus _____
6. diminished _____

A. started
B. noise
C. annoying or bothering
D. became less or decreased
E. fearing
F. expected

B. **Read each sentence. Find a synonym from the word box for each underlined word. Re-write each sentence.**

extremely   thorough   generous   swiftly   startling   weary
concerned   scrumptious   brief   lengthy   enjoyable

1. The <u>caring</u> counsellor took a <u>complete</u> look around for poison ivy.

   _____

   _____

2. We heard a scary noise and ran <u>fast</u> to our cabin.

   _____

   _____

3. Although my time at camp was <u>short</u>, I had a <u>fun</u> experience.

   _____

   _____

4. They gave <u>big</u> portions of dessert and it was always <u>good</u>.

   _____

   _____

5. By the end of our <u>long</u> hiking excursion, I felt <u>really</u> <u>tired</u>.

   _____

   _____

C. Write a journal entry for the fourth day at Camp Wannastay. Remember to date the entry and include this camper's thoughts, feelings, and opinions about Camp Wannastay.

_____

_____

_____

_____

_____

_____

_____

D. Write the past tense verbs for the following words. Each word has the letters "gh" in it, which are silent.

> When the letters "gh" are together, they are usually **silent**, as in "ni**gh**t".

1. buy _____
2. catch _____
3. fight _____
4. bring _____
5. think _____
6. teach _____

E. Write a word ending with the letters "gh" to match each clue.

> Sometimes "gh" at the end of a word makes an "**f**" **sound**, as in "enou**gh**".

1. antonym of "smooth" _____
2. what you do when something is funny _____
3. when you have an itchy throat _____
4. what a horse drinks from _____
5. meat that is not tender _____

F. **Design a colourful poster to advertise Camp Wannastay the way you imagine it.**

1. Include descriptions of the following:
   a. the cabins and the property around the camp area
   b. activities to participate in – daytime and evening
   c. the people that work there (experience and qualifications)
2. Include quotations of what other campers say about their experience at Camp Wannastay.
3. Include illustrations.

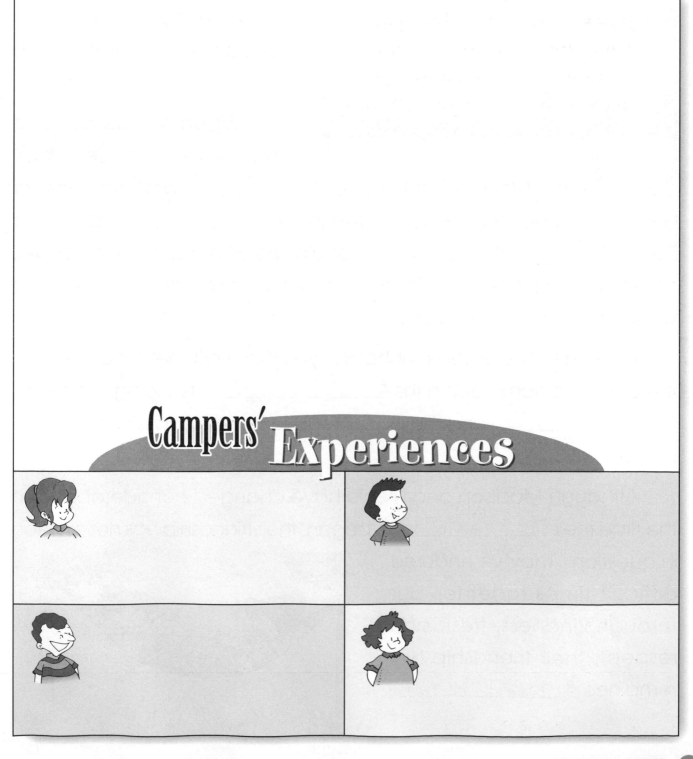

Campers' Experiences

PROGRESS TEST 2

A. Complete this story by filling in the blanks with the words provided.

jokes	strong	backyard
company	groovy	best
clubhouse	relationship	

Nicole and Madison really enjoy each other's 1._____ . They've been great pals since the time they were born because their mothers are 2._____ of friends.

When Nicole goes to Madison's house, they disappear into Madison's private 3._____ and are gone for hours. The clubhouse is decorated in a 4._____ style and has all the comforts of home. It's equipped with a CD player, books, crafts, board games, comfy chairs, and even a miniature fridge. It's a wonder they ever come out.

After they tire of the clubhouse, you can find them lounging on the giant-size hammock in the 5._____ . Hanging out, telling 6._____ , and sharing secrets seem to be a satisfying pastime for them.

Although Madison and Nicole have changed considerably from the time their 7._____ began, their friendship has never been in question. They've endured difficult times together, but through kindness, trust, and respect, their friendship has remained 8._____ .

B. Underline the base word in each of the following.

1. un<u>success</u>ful
2. <u>fright</u>ful
3. dis<u>appear</u>

4. <u>end</u>less
5. <u>wonder</u>ful
6. <u>perform</u>ance

7. <u>friend</u>liest
8. <u>sudden</u>ly
9. un<u>believe</u>able

C. Build words that match the clues below using each suffix once.

-able -ist -er -ful -or -less -ness -ly

1. full of wonder _____

2. one who performs _____

3. one who writes novels _____

4. without thought _____

5. able to laugh _____

6. in a careful way or manner _____

7. one who sails _____

8. state of being happy _____

D. Write homophones for these words.

1. board _____
2. sent _____

3. their _____
4. where _____

5. been _____
6. knew _____

7. through _____
8. I _____

9. hours _____
10. ate _____

E. **Sort these words under the correct sensory heading.**

bright   spicy   silky   fruity   blurry   swishing   bitter   squishy
shiny   skunky   fuzzy   crackling   rotten   tangy   whistling

Sight   _____   _____   _____

Sound   _____   _____   _____

Smell   _____   _____   _____

Taste   _____   _____   _____

Touch   _____   _____

F. **Re-write each sentence in the past tense.**

1. We practise our dance moves until we master them.

   _____

2. Madison and Nicole will attend each other's parties.

   _____

3. We study many school subjects together.

   _____

G. **Find and underline 5 transition words from the paragraph below.**

Madison and Nicole keep themselves busy when they're together. First, they disappear into the clubhouse for a game of cards. Then, they check out the fridge for snacks and drinks. After their snack break, Nicole and Madison listen to music. Before they head out to the backyard, they play a board game or two. Finally, they settle in for secrets on the hammock.

H. Find ten pairs of synonyms. List them on the lines below.

brief	bright	ruckus	wonder	swift	many	start
oldest	fast	pester	eldest	initiate	short	annoy
vivid	numerous	victory	win	marvel	noisy	

1. _____ , _____   2. _____ , _____

3. _____ , _____   4. _____ , _____

5. _____ , _____   6. _____ , _____

7. _____ , _____   8. _____ , _____

9. _____ , _____   10. _____ , _____

I. Select a word from the choices below that describe the writer's tone in each sentence. Write it on the line.

frustrated	funny	sad	frightened
excited	happy	angry	serious

1. _____ Her body shivered when she heard an unfamiliar sound in the basement.

2. _____ I have been waiting so long for the party day to arrive and it's finally here.

3. _____ Saying good-bye is difficult because we only see each other twice a year.

4. _____ Mom made my favourite cookies to share with my friends at the sleepover.

5. _____ My little sister scribbled all over my homework.

J.   Circle the onomatopoeia word in each sentence.

1. The chirping birds woke us very early in the morning.

2. We were frightened at the sudden boom of thunder.

3. I accidentally dropped the bowl of freshly popped popcorn.

4. We clanged our glasses together and toasted our friendship.

5. The mosquitoes buzzed around us while we chatted outdoors.

K.   Choose one of the prefixes to complete the word. Under each sentence, write the meaning of this new word.

| dis | mis | pre | un | bi | tri | re | mid |

1. The girls had a _____understanding, but they solved it quickly.

    Meaning: _____

2. Sometimes it's best to agree than to _____agree.

    Meaning: _____

3. We were allowed to stay up until _____night.

    Meaning: _____

4. The blue, red, and silver _____coloured room was unusual.

    Meaning: _____

5. The mothers _____arranged a surprise visit for their girls.

    Meaning: _____

6. They were asked to _____lock the door to the clubhouse.

    Meaning: _____

L. Match the phrases to create similes. Write the corresponding letters in the boxes.

1. They ran as fast   ⬚   A. as a sleepy bear.

2. Her sweater felt as soft   ⬚   B. like a mischievous monkey.

3. Nicole swims   ⬚   C. as a tired snail.

4. She was as grumpy   ⬚   D. like frosty popsicles.

5. Ben walks as slowly   ⬚   E. as a speeding fighter jet.

6. That child climbs trees   ⬚   F. as a kitten's fur.

7. My fingers were frozen   ⬚   G. like fleeting fish.

M. Write the letter of the correct answer to each question.

1. Which word contains a prefix?   _____
   A. unity   B. present
   C. disappear   D. middle

2. Which is an example of alliteration?   _____
   A. The rattling windows kept us awake.
   B. She is as wise as an old owl.
   C. Nervous Nicole now knows the new neighbour.
   D. Her fingernails are as hard as nails.

3. Which word is an example of a noun?   _____

   Which word is an example of a verb?   _____

   Which word is an example of an adjective?   _____

   Which word is an example of an adverb?   _____
   A. groovy   B. happily
   C. clubhouse   D. sing

Welcome

Language Games

1

Write what Mokki the Alien is saying to the children. Use the code to help you.

A	B	C	D	E	F	G	H	I	J	K	L	M

N	O	P	Q	R	S	T	U	V	W	X	Y	Z

_____

_____

_____

2

Complete the word slides to turn "mice" into "mist". Change only one letter for each slide.

m | i | c | e

m | i | □ | e

m | i | n | □

m | i | □ | t

Complete the word slides to turn "coin" into "burn". Change only one letter for each slide.

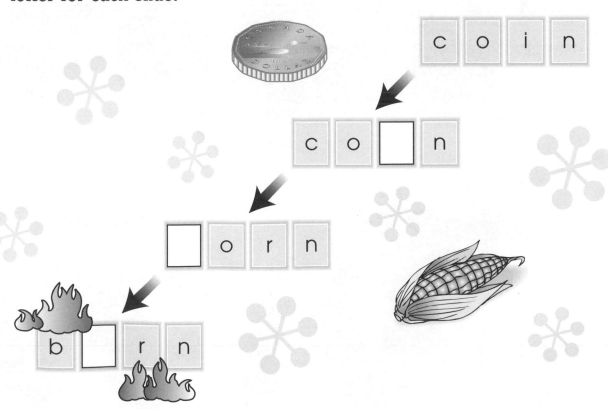

c | o | i | n

c | o | □ | n

□ | o | r | n

b | □ | r | n

3 Circle the word that does not rhyme in each set.

1.

fish   dish   rich   wish

2.

duck   tuck   luck   back

3.

star   jar   for   car

4.

lock   look   book   hook

5.

share   bear   pear   dear

4 Complete the crossword puzzle with words that rhyme with the clue words.

**cross**

A. light   B. sleep
C. sigh   D. love
E. hand   F. might

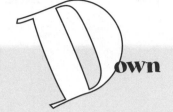**own**

1. steal   2. tame
3. plain   4. power
5. sale   6. loose
7. bend

Rhyming Crossword Puzzle

5 Complete the word slides to turn "cone" into "tube". Change only one letter for each slide.

c o n e

☐ o n e

t ☐ n e

t u ☐ e

Complete the word slides to turn "sail" into "tell". Change only one letter for each slide.

s a i l

☐ a i l

t a ☐ l

t ☐ l l

6

Circle the twelve months of a year in the word search.

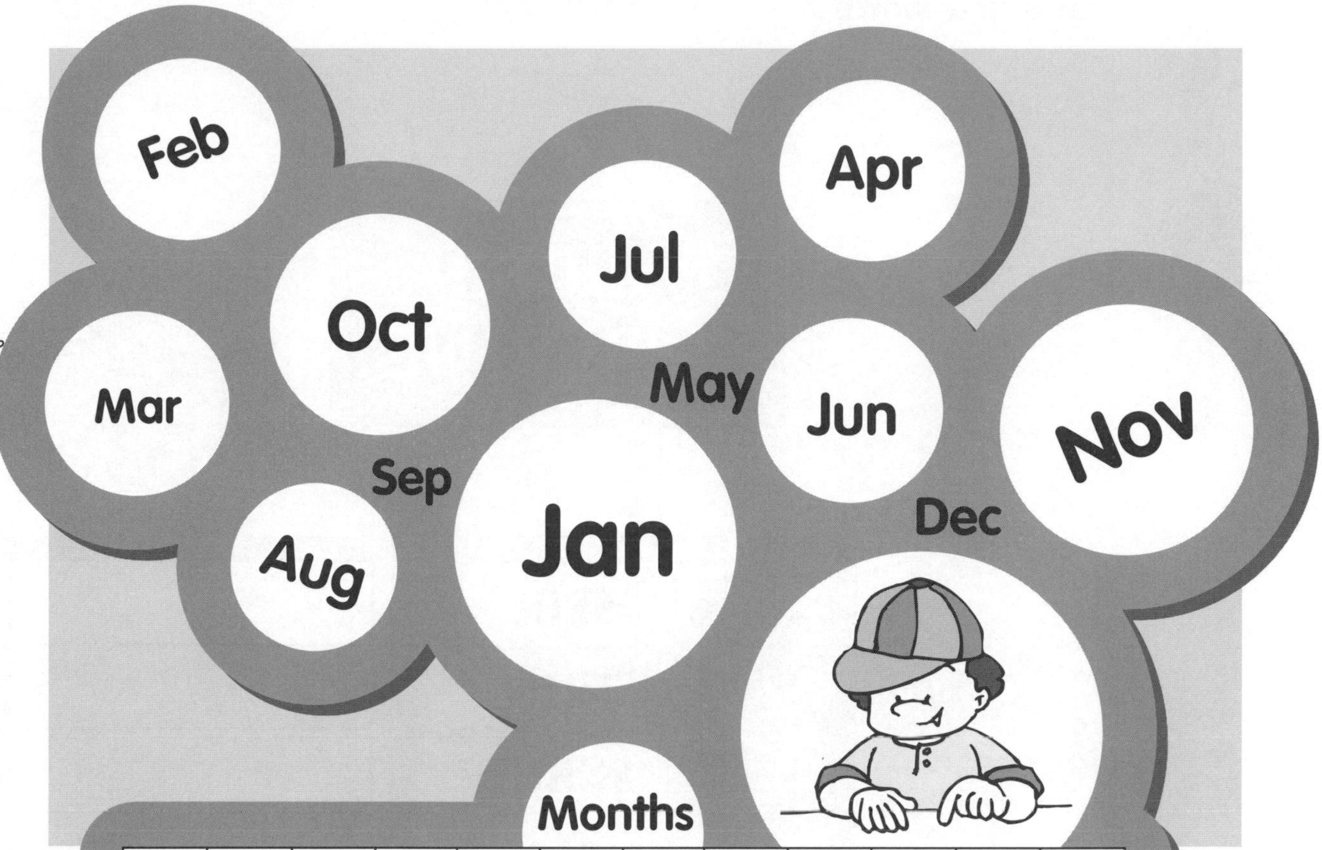

Feb

Apr

Jul

Oct

Mar

May

Jun

Nov

Sep

Jan

Dec

Aug

Months

l	D	j	f	n	D	A	u	g	u	s	t
F	e	O	A	J	h	e	O	l	e	i	d
j	c	b	c	M	a	r	c	h	k	u	N
S	e	J	J	t	N	n	c	S	F	o	h
A	m	g	u	D	o	a	u	M	e	J	k
h	b	M	l	n	v	b	s	a	b	t	a
m	e	o	y	F	e	N	e	y	r	s	y
s	r	e	m	V	m	b	w	r	u	y	n
O	b	J	i	O	b	e	M	g	a	z	k
n	S	e	p	t	e	m	b	e	r	x	p
j	a	k	A	p	r	i	l	c	y	d	r
c	e	o	M	g	D	f	d	i	l	m	e

7 Help Jerry insert the letter blocks into the words in the word machine to form new words.

WORD MACHINE

T	SEAL	1
K	THIN	2
C	SCARE	3
A	SET	4
I	CHEF	5
L	FIGHT	6
R	GAIN	7
S	EXIT	8
W	SING	9
E	TUB	10
P	RELY	11
O	BAT	12

8

Complete the word slides to turn "rose" into "dice". Change only one letter for each slide.

r o s e

r [ ] s e

r i [ ] e

[ ] i c e

Complete the word slides to turn "near" into "bean". Change only one letter for each slide.

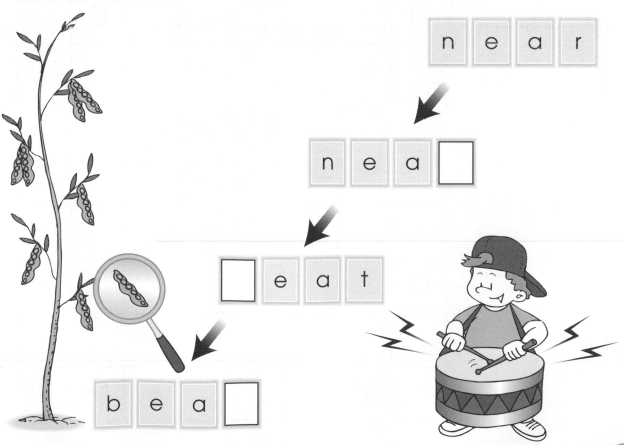

n e a r

n e a [ ]

[ ] e a t

b e a [ ]

9

Help Marco the Mouse get to the centre of the maze to meet his friends.
Write the plural of each noun.

1 elf 2 ox 3 city

4 deer 5 moose 6 man

7 goose 8 hero 9 child 10 mouse

Complete the crossword puzzle with a homonym for each clue word.

Across

A. stair
B. tear
C. moose
D. steel
E. ice
F. no

Down

1. caught
2. eight
3. blue
4. right
5. so
6. sell

Homonym

ate = **?**

11 Help Little Worm get to the core of the apple by following the "fruit" words.

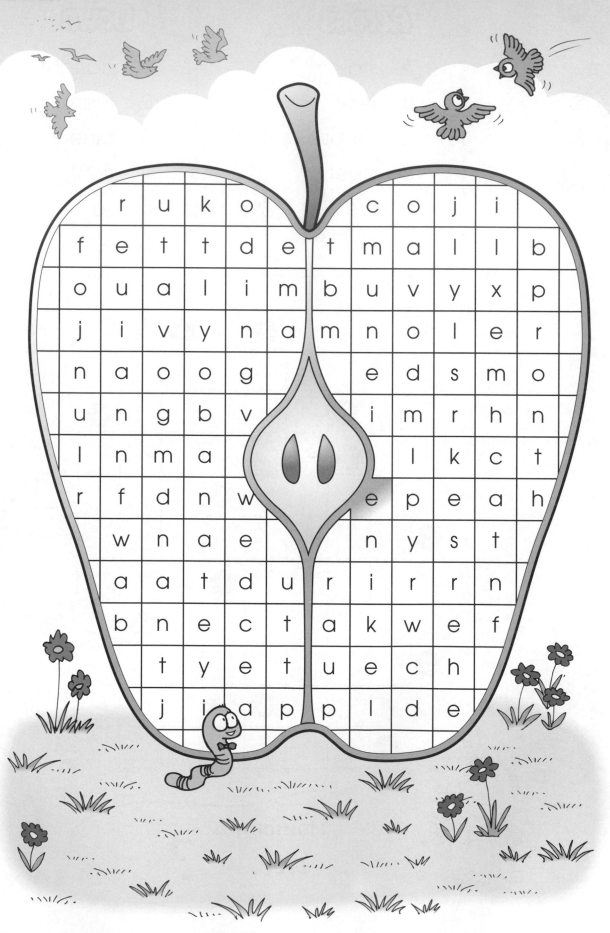

r	u	k	o		c	o	j	i
f	e	t	t	d	e	t	m	a	l	l	b
o	u	a	l	i	m	b	u	v	y	x	p
j	i	v	y	n	a	m	n	o	l	e	r
n	a	o	o	g		e	d	s	m	o
u	n	g	b	v		i	m	r	h	n
l	n	m	a			l	k	c	t
r	f	d	n	w	e	p	e	a	h
w	n	a	e		n	y	s	t
a	a	t	d	u	r	i	r	r	n
b	n	e	c	t	a	k	w	e	f
t	y	e	t	u	e	c	h
j	i	a	p	p	l	d	e

12

Complete the word slides to turn "wise" into "wind".
Change only one letter for each slide.

w i s e

↓

w i ☐ e

↓

w i ☐ e

↓

w i n ☐

Complete the word slides to turn "belt" into "wall". Change only one letter for each slide.

b e l t

↓

b e l ☐

↓

☐ e l l

↓

w ☐ l l

13 Write five 3-letter words with the letters in each group.

1. | P | R | E | A |

_____
_____
_____
_____
_____

2. | B | E | L | E | T |

_____
_____
_____
_____

3. | G | M | T | N | E |

_____
_____
_____
_____

4. | H | R | S | T | I |

_____
_____
_____
_____

14

Look at each picture. Circle the correctly-spelled word in each pair.

1.

kangeroo
kangaroo

2.

alien
alein

3.

statue
statute

4.

hammar
hammer

5.

folk
fork

6.

turtle
turtal

7.

toboggan
tobaggan

8.

envelop
envelope

9.

vedio game
video game

15

Complete the word slides to turn "road" into "near".
Change only one letter for each slide.

| r | o | a | d |

| r | o | a | ☐ |

| r | ☐ | a | r |

| ☐ | e | a | r |

Complete the word slides to turn "bear" into "heat". Change only one letter for each slide.

| b | e | a | r |

| b | e | a | ☐ |

| ☐ | e | a | d |

| h | e | a | ☐ |

16

Circle twelve vegetables in the Vegetable Word Search.

VEGETABLE Word Search

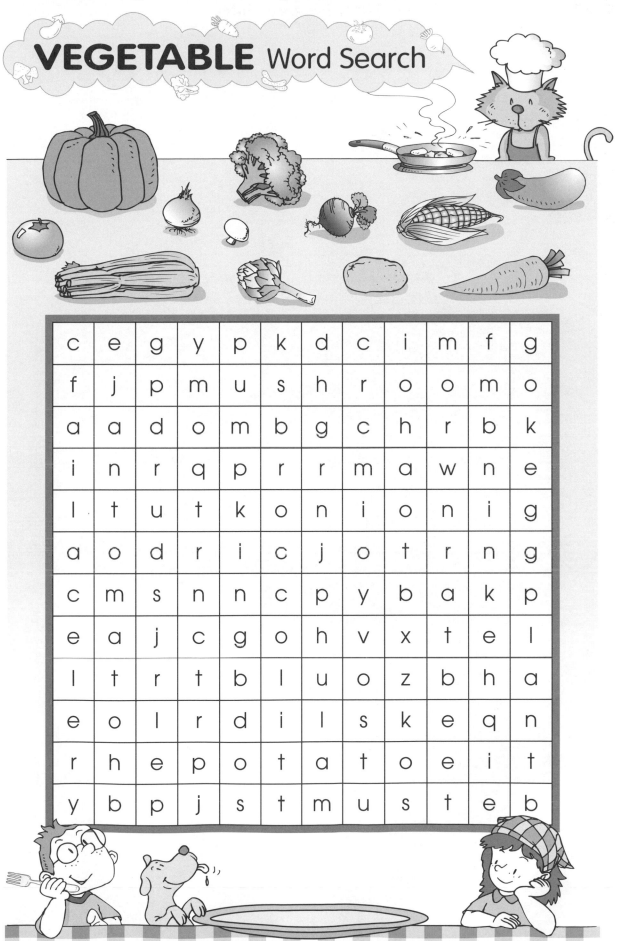

c	e	g	y	p	k	d	c	i	m	f	g
f	j	p	m	u	s	h	r	o	o	m	o
a	a	d	o	m	b	g	c	h	r	b	k
i	n	r	q	p	r	r	m	a	w	n	e
l	t	u	t	k	o	n	i	o	n	i	g
a	o	d	r	i	c	j	o	t	r	n	g
c	m	s	n	n	c	p	y	b	a	k	p
e	a	j	c	g	o	h	v	x	t	e	l
l	t	r	t	b	l	u	o	z	b	h	a
e	o	l	r	d	i	l	s	k	e	q	n
r	h	e	p	o	t	a	t	o	e	i	t
y	b	p	j	s	t	m	u	s	t	e	b

1 Ghosts

A. 1. T   2. T   3. F   4. F
   5. T   6. T   7. F   8. T
B. 1. B   2. C   3. D   4. A
C. (Answers will vary.)
D. 1. cried   2. tired
   3. ran   4. find
   5. behave   6. walked
   7. hears   8. delicious
E. 1. F   2. D   3. G   4. C
   5. B   6. H   7. E   8. A
F. 1. H   2. F   3. G   4. J
   5. C   6. K   7. B   8. D
   9. E   10. A   11. I
G. (Answers will vary.)

2 The Human Heart

A. 1. A   2. B   3. C   4. C
   5. B   6. A
B. 1. E   2. A   3. B   4. C
   5. F   6. D
C. 1. played ; A   2. flew ; A
   3. is ; N   4. were ; N
   5. is ; N   6. sang ; A
   7. was ; N   8. cross ; A
   9. studied ; scored ; A 10. is ; is ; N
D. 1. went   2. flew
   3. sailed   4. camped
   5. built   6. stayed
   7. took
E.

3 The First Heart Transplant

A. 1. O   2. F   3. O   4. F
   5. O   6. F   7. F   8. O
   9. F   10. O   11. F   12. O

13. O   14. O
B. (Answers will vary.)
C. 1. He | played   2. parents | told
   3. presents | were   4. friend | is
   5. two | make   6. They | played
D. 1. D   2. E   3. A   4. B
   5. C
E. (Answers will vary.)
F. 1. its   2. their
   3. here   4. dairy
   5. feat   6. fourth
   7. dual   8. weather
   9. too   10. loose
   11. dessert   12. cloths
G. (Answers will vary.)

4 The Incredible Butterfly

A. 1. They have beautiful colours.
   2. They pollinate plants when they feed.
   3. Some use their colour as camouflage while others use their bright colour as a warning to predators. The Magnificent Owl butterfly's large dot on its wing makes predators think that it is a much larger animal.
B. 1. egg   2. larva
   3. pupa   4. adult
C. 1. nectar   2. proboscis
   3. flower   4. pupa
   5. world   6. Magnificent Owl
   7. Monarch
D. (Answers will vary.)
E. (Answers will vary.)
F. 1. transformation   2. warning
   3. creations   4. widest
   5. diversity   6. tropical
   7. beautiful   8. depending
G. 1. exchange ; changeable
   2. imprint ; printing
   3. impolite ; politeness
   4. disbelieve ; believable
   5. impatient ; patience
   6. unreal ; realistic
   7. indefinite ; definitely
   8. misbehave ; behaviour
   9. disappoint ; appointment
   10. insincere ; sincerity

5 The Atlas

A. 1. G   2. E   3. D   4. F
   5. H   6. J   7. I   8. A
   9. C   10. B

B. 1. Atlantic   2. Pacific
   3. Indian   4. Arctic
   5. Antarctic

C. Australasia ; Asia ; Europe ; Africa ; South America ; North America ; Antarctica

D. 1. excited ; loud
   2. tall ; husky ; heavy
   3. tired ; warm
   4. expensive ; top ; antique
   5. shiny ; new ; red ; perfect ; birthday

E. 1. gallantly
   2. bravely ; courageously
   3. silently ; quickly
   4. never
   5. proudly ; brilliantly

F. 1. imaginary   2. equator
   3. entire   4. grids
   5. circles   6. exact
   7. scale   8. prime
   9. latitude   10. sections

G. (Answers will vary.)

6 Disasters at Sea (1)

A. 1. F   2. F   3. T   4. F
   5. T   6. F   7. T   8. T
   9. F   10. T   11. T   12. F

B. (Answers will vary.)

C. 1. The parents watched their children play hockey game.
   2. The birthday cake had nine candles on it.
   3. The father and his son went fishing in the lake.
   4. When school ended, the summer holidays began.

D. (Answers will vary.)

E. 1. many   2. disasters
   3. left   4. expensive
   5. fancy   6. large
   7. struck   8. luxurious

F. (Answer will vary.)

7 Disasters at Sea (2)

A. 1. 2   2. 1   3. 3

B. 1. May 7, 1915 ; November 21, 1916
   2. passenger ship ; hospital ship
   3. torpedoed ; hit a mine or torpedoed
   4. 18 minutes ; 55 minutes

C. 1. his   2. her
   3. he   4. their ; their
   5. our ; theirs   6. our ; it
   7. them

D. 1. Which   2. Who
   3. Whose   4. What
   5. Which

E. 1. spacious   2. elegant
   3. scrumptious   4. frequently
   5. drenched   6. delicious
   7. elated   8. depressing
   9. chilly   10. swiftly

F. (Answers will vary.)

8 Education in the Renaissance

A. (Suggested answers)
   1. Pupils listened to the teacher reading from a book and often memorized his words. Tests were taken orally.
   2. They learned sewing, cooking, dancing, and the basics of taking care of a household at home.
   3. Scholars at that time conducted experiments in search of answers to the mysteries of the universe.
   4. His theories went against Church beliefs (that the earth was the centre of the universe).

B. 1. brother   2. cabinet
   3. tennis   4. me
   5. papers   6. thief
   7. passengers   8. breakfast
   9. dress ; shoes   10. flowers

C. (Answers will vary.)

D. (Answers will vary.)

E. (Answers will vary.)

9 Plants – Nature's Medicine

A. 1. I   2. F   3. G   4. H
   5. C   6. D   7. E   8. J
   9. B   10. A

B. 1. T   2. F   3. F   4. T
   5. T   6. F   7. T   8. F
   9. T   10. T

C. 1. me   2. mother
   3. Cathy   4. pupils
   5. son   6. sister

7. us   8. him
9. mechanic   10. him
D. (Answers will vary.)
E. 1. deadly   2. benefits
3. common   4. valuable
5. slower   6. helps
7. popular   8. illness
9. ancient   10. medicinal
11. certain   12. produces

Progress Test 1

A. 1. T   2. F   3. F   4. T
5. F   6. F   7. T   8. F
9. T   10. T   11. T   12. F
13. T   14. F   15. F   16. T
17. T   18. T
B. 1. C   2. B   3. A   4. C
5. C   6. A   7. B   8. C
9. A   10. B   11. C   12. A
C. 1. She ; (likes) ; ice cream ; day
2. He ; (tripped) ; shoelace ; (fell) ; stairs
3. weather ; (was)
4. boys ; girls ; (played) ; yard
5. Jim ; John ; Sam ; (walked) ; school
6. Linda ; (is) ; years ; Susan
7. neighbours ; (held) ; sale ; street
8. Winter ; (is) ; season
9. Time ; (is wasted) ; we ; (do) nothing
10. clock ; (struck) ; three , bell , (rang)
D. (Answers may vary.)
1. B   2. A   3. F   4. C
5. G   6. E   7. D
E. 1. their   2. She
3. me ; his   4. They
5. she
F. 1. blazing ; slowly
2. happy ; birthday ; quickly
3. Slowly ; surely ; skilled
4. tall ; immediately ; basketball
5. swiftly ; stone ; sandy
G. 1. me ; ball
2. Janet
3. son ; bicycle
4. back ; ball
5. us ; chance
H. 1. D   2. I   3. J   4. A
5. K   6. C   7. L   8. E
9. H   10. G   11. B   12. F

I. 1. diary   2. They're
3. fourth   4. feat
5. whether   6. duel
7. too   8. hear
J. 1. unreal   2. insincere
3. indirect   4. impatient
5. disbelief   6. unknown
7. improper   8. misbehave
9. uncertain   10. unbelievable
11. reliable   12. dependable
13. riding   14. happiness
15. crying   16. appointment
K. 1. delicious   2. hilarious
3. bitterly   4. kind ; elderly
5. drenched ; pelting   6. spacious ; antique

10 J.K. Rowling – Her Story

A. 1. B   2. B   3. C   4. B
5. A
B. (Answer will vary.)
C. 1. Look out! ; Excl.
2. Stop before it's too late! ; Excl.
3. I think it is time to leave. ; Decl.
4. The sun is shining today. ; Decl.
5. Where did I put my wallet? ; Int.
6. Where did he go after school? ; Int.
7. Wash your hands before dinner. ; Imp.
8. Pick up those books on the floor. ; Imp.
D. (Answers will vary.)
E. 1. run   2. called
3. growled/growls   4. beautiful
5. helpful   6. careful
7. kindness   8. formation
9. solution   10. terribly
11. movement   12. celebration
F. 1. un   2. dis   3. un   4. im
5. im   6. dis   7. dis   8. un
9. un   10. in   11. un   12. im

11 Games and Toys of Pioneer Canada (1)

A. (Answers will vary.)
B. (Answers will vary.)
C. 1. She screamed, "Look out!"
2. Linda yelled, "Is anyone there?"
3. He played baseball, soccer, basketball, and hockey.

4. "Let's go swimming," said Janet to her friends.
5. The teacher said, "Tonight, for homework, you have Math, Science, and Spelling."

D. (Answer will vary.)
E. (Answers will vary.)

12 Games and Toys of Pioneer Canada (2)

A.
1. a stuffed pig's bladder
2. a pigskin
3. hoop rolling
4. a silhouette
5. dolls
6. a tree branch
7. no automobiles

B. 1. O   2. O   3. O   4. F
   5. F

C. (Answers will vary.)

D. 1. star   2. canoe
   3. pots   4. peach
   5. cloud

E. 1. wear   2. hear
   3. threw   4. mane
   5. weak   6. sail

13 Medieval Castles

A. 1. B   2. B   3. A   4. A
   5. C   6. C

B. 1. sky   2. morning
   3. pond   4. school
   5. rain

C. 1. moon   2. tuffet
   3. hill   4. wall
   5. clock

D. (Answers will vary.)

E. 1. knives   2. lives
   3. halves
      the "f" or "fe" to "ves"
   4. armies   5. diaries
   6. cities   7. ladies
      "y" and add "ies"
   8. journeys   9. keys
   10. valleys
       "s"

F. 1. geese   2. children
   3. feet   4. men
   5. teeth   6. mice
   7. The singular and plural are the same.

14 The Thinking Organ

A. 1. organ   2. growing
   3. process   4. memory
   5. emotions   6. cerebrum
   7. cerebellum   8. left
   9. hypothalamus 10. nervous

B. 1. E   2. D   3. B   4. C
   5. F   6. A

C. (Answer will vary.)

D. 1. and   2. unless
   3. since   4. because
   5. or   6. while
   7. but   8. if
   9. so   10. until

E. 1. complex   2. dominant
   3. amazing   4. organs
   5. mystery   6. emotions
   7. connected   8. fear
   9. vital   10. creative
   11. function   12. stored

F. (Answers will vary.)

15 The Origins of Money

A. (Suggestions only)
   1a. credit card   b. debit card
   c. cheque   d. cash
   2. It means trading.
   3a. shells   b. feathers
   c. tools   d. jewelry
   4. The item being used for currency directly represented the item being purchased.
   5. They could be killed for food or used for work.
   6. The shrewdest trader profited the most.

B. (Answers will vary.)

C. 1. in the kennel
   2. of grade four ; (in his desk)
   3. (In the morning) ; (over the cliffs)
   4. (under the desk)
   5. (up the road) ; (down the hill)
   6. (Under the rainbow) ; of gold

D. (Answers will vary.)
E. (Answers will vary.)

16 New France – The Beginning of Canada (1)

A. 1. T   2. T   3. F   4. T
   5. T   6. T   7. F   8. T

9. T   10. F   11. T   12. T

B. 1. 1534 ; 1535
    2. 2 ships, 60 men ; 3 ships, 110 men
    3. Explored P.E.I. and New Brunswick, clamied land for France, brought back Donnaconna's sons ; Reached Montreal, named village Mount Réal.

C.   In the month of June, Professor Smith took his wife Mary and his children, Jake, Mark, and Jordan, on a fishing trip up to Moon River in the Muskoka area of Northern Ontario. The drive from Toronto took three hours but they stopped for lunch at McDonald's. Because the drive was so long, Jordan brought his book entitled The Best Way To Catch Fish. He thought this book might help him learn how to fish. He was going to use the special fish hook called a Surehook that he received for a birthday gift in May. It was made by Acme Fishing Gear Company located in Montreal. When they arrived, they passed the old St. Luke's Church down the road from the river. Working outside the church was Pastor Rodgers, who also likes to fish. He waved at them as they went by.

D. 1.
```
    R
D I S C O V E R
    U
    T
    E
```
2.
```
  I
  M
I M P A S S A B L E
  R
  E
  S
  S
```
3.
```
    F
    O
E X P L O R E D
    T
    H
    O
    L
    D
```
4.
```
      O
      N
E S T A B L I S H E D
      E
      T
```
5.
```
  S
  H
C O N V I N C E D
  R
  T
  A
  G
  E
```
6.
```
  R
  I
S E V E R E
  A
  L
  S
```

17 New France – The Beginning of Canada (2)

A. 1. O   2. O   3. F   4. F
    5. O   6. F   7. F   8. O
    9. O   10. O
B. (Answers will vary.)
C. (Suggestion only)
    He overlooked the furs of the woodland animals such as fox and beaver.

D. (Answers will vary.)
E. 1. Carol called on Julie but Julie was not home.
    2. Because Friday is a holiday, there is no school.
    3. My grade four teacher, Mrs Smith, is very nice.
    4. Philip had a doctor's appointment on Tuesday.
F. Crossword A

```
      ❶
      S
❹M I S E R Y
      T
      T
      L
❻P R E P A R E
```

Crossword B

```
  ❶
❹T H I N K
  A
  R
❻D E V E L O P
```

Crossword C

```
  ❶        ❷
          A
❹F I G H T
  A       A
  I       C
  L       K
```

Progress Test 2

A. 1. B   2. B   3. A   4. C
    5. B   6. A   7. C   8. A
    9. C   10. C   11. C   12. A
    13. C   14. B   15. A   16. C
    17. C   18. B   19. A   20. B
    21. C   22. C

B. 1. Get up, you're going to be late. ; imperative
    2. Who will help with the work? ; interrogative
    3. Wow! ; exclamatory
    4. This is the main street in town. ; declarative
C. 1. When the storm ended, we came out to play.
    2. I played basketball, hockey, football, and tennis.
    3. She said to the new student, "Take any seat you like."
    4. Peaches, plums, pears, and nectarines are expensive in winter.
    5. He shouted, "Let me in, it's cold outside!"
D. 1. under   2. in
    3. around   4. in
    5. down

E. 1. Under the rug ; of dirt
    2. into the pool
    3. in the local school ; at the fundraising
    4. In the morning ; to her friend ; in the other part ; of town

F. 1. or   2. or
    3. although   4. but
    5. if

G. 1. ADV   2. ADJ
    3. ADJ ; ADV   4. ADV
    5. ADJ

H. 1. Mr. Smith asked John to meet him at Lions Stadium.
    2. She said, "Could someone please assist me?"
    3. Lauren and Kara read a Judy Blume story.
    4. He worked at the Ministry of Transport in downtown Montreal.
    5. They rented a cottage on Rice Lake in the Kawartha region.

I. 1. G   2. H   3. I   4. O
    5. K   6. B   7. L   8. M
    9. N   10. E   11. F   12. A
    13. C   14. J   15. D

J. 1. laughed   2. beautiful
    3. chirping   4. dangerous
    5. performing   6. happily
    7. donation   8. reliable
    9. made   10. lively
    11. terrified

K. 1. heroes   2. armies
    3. cities   4. ladies
    5. lives   6. leaves
    7. halves   8. tomatoes
    9. potatoes   10. mice

L. (Suggestions only)
    1. arrangement   2. disorganize
    3. preview   4. disconnect
    5. remind   6. appointment
    7. unsatisfied   8. creative
    9. disbelief   10. careless

1 Nouns

A. 1. jumps   2. bulky   3. sings
   4. exciting   5. useful   6. happy
B. 1. Harry Potter   2. Joe Sakic
   3. CN Tower   4. Royal Bank
   5. Air Canada Centre   6. Wonderland
C. 1. <u>Ramon Gonzales</u> and his <u>sister</u>, <u>Julia</u>, attend <u>Williamson Road Public School</u>.
   2. They enjoy playing <u>sports</u> at recess <u>time</u>.
   3. <u>Ramon</u> is a very good basketball <u>player</u> while <u>Julia</u> prefers to play <u>volleyball</u>.
   4. The Gonzales <u>family</u> moved to <u>Canada</u> from <u>Spain</u> three <u>years</u> ago and live in a downtown <u>neighbourhood</u>.
   5. <u>Julia</u> and <u>Ramon</u> speak both <u>Spanish</u> and <u>English</u> and are learning <u>French</u> in <u>school</u>.
   6. <u>Mr. Gonzales</u> works as a computer <u>programmer</u> and <u>Mrs. Gonzales</u> is an interior <u>decorator</u>.
   7. In the Gonzales <u>family</u> there are four <u>children</u>, but only <u>two</u> of the <u>children</u> attend <u>school</u>.
   8. Next <u>summer</u>, the <u>family</u> will visit their <u>cousins</u> in <u>Spain</u>.
D. 1. armies – 4a   2. lunches – 3
   3. pens – 1   4. duties – 4a
   5. proofs – 2   6. ladies – 4a
   7. lives – 2   8. journeys – 4b
   9. halves – 2   10. patios – 5a
   11. taxes – 3   12. radios – 5a
   13. cars – 1   14. diaries – 4a
   15. churches – 3   16. leaves – 2
Challenge
   1. These nouns are both singular and plural.
   2. A. oxen   B. mice
      C. children   D. teeth
E. A. crew   B. team   C. gang
   D. army   E. navy
   1. nation   2. company   3. crowd

2 Pronouns

A. 1. it   2. their   3. her   4. us
   5. their   6. us   7. it   8. We
   9. me   10. hers
B. 1. them   2. us   3. whom   4. her
   5. him   6. me   7. her
C. 1. her   2. his   3. their   4. our
   5. yours ; mine
D. 1. Which   2. Whose / What
   3. Who   4. Where
E. 1. It   2. They   3. their   4. Their
   5. them   6. him   7. them   8. they
   9. their   10. His   11. he   12. them
   13. their   14. They   15. them   16. they
   17. whom
Challenge
   1. her – John tied his shoe.
   2. ourselves – The boys kept the candy to themselves.
   3. who – John wasn't sure to whom he should call.
   4. our – The audience clapped their hands.
   5. my – We took our time getting here.
   a. themselves – We helped ourselves to the treats.
   b. Whom – Who is at the door?
   c. his – Cheryl hurt her foot.
   d. our – I walked home on my own.
   e. their – We raised our voices in the singing.

3 Adjectives

A. 1. tall ; his ; small
   2. cold ; tired
   3. deep ; older ; huge ; snow
   4. bright ; dark
   5. this ; adventure ; younger
   6. little ; short ; sweet
B. 1. small – smaller – smallest
   2. early – earlier – earliest
   3. happy – happier – happiest
   4. sad – sadder – saddest
   5. cheap – cheaper – cheapest
   6. fine – finer – finest
   7. kind – kinder – kindest
   8. new – newer – newest
C. 1. good – better – best   2. much – more – most
   3. bad – worse – worst   4. some – more – most
   5. little – less – least
D. 1. a   2. b   3. a   4. a
   5. a   6. b
E. 1. F   2. D   3. C   4. E
   5. G   6. H   7. A   8. B
F. (Suggested answers)
   1. hottest   2. wise   3. local
   4. bus   5. most   6. cool
   7. No Swimming   8. disappointed   9. public
   10. spacious

4 Adverbs

A. 2. loudly – how   3. always – when
   4. quickly – how   5. slowly – how
   6. soon – when   7. sincerely – how
   8. accurately – how ; quickly – how
   9. busily – how
   10. faster – how ; farther – where
   11. slightly – how
B. 1. entirely   2. greedily   3. fairly
   4. simply   5. sloppily   6. happily
   7. desperately   8. nicely   9. silently
   10. wearily
C. 1. <u>lazily</u> (along)   2. <u>sickly</u> (sweet)
   3. <u>incredibly</u> (early)   4. <u>entirely</u> (pleased)
   5. <u>desperately</u> (hungry)   6. <u>fairly</u> (dark)
   7. <u>badly</u> (injured)   8. <u>completely</u> (useless)
D. 1. He rides his bicycle more carefully than his brother.

2. He played hockey more skilfully than all his team-mates.
3. The dogs in the cage barked more viciously than the dogs on leashes.
4. The librarian spoke more enthusiastically than our teacher about the book.
5. Her homework was more carefully done than mine.

E. 1. bad – worse – worst   2. well – better – best
   3. badly – worse – worst

F. 1. excitedly   2. finally   3. vigorously
   4. kindly   5. generously   6. wildly
   7. dangerously   8. incredibly   9. easily

5 Verbs

A. 1. were playing   2. made
   3. arrived ; phoned   4. rang ; began
   5. ran ; sat ; watched

B. 1. The parents applauded the (performance) of the party.
   2. He shot the (puck) into the net.
   3. The girls in the class sang a (song) while the boys performed a (dance).
   4. The bus driver took the passengers' (tickets) before leaving the depot.
   5. The children played (baseball) in the schoolyard while the teachers held a (meeting).

C. 1. asked – T   2. ask – T   3. was – I
   4. raced – I   5. played – T

D. 1. will   2. has   3. will
   4. must   5. will

E. 2. catch – caught – catching – caught
   3. cut – cut – cutting – cut
   4. become – became – becoming – become
   5. draw – drew – drawing – drawn
   6. know – knew – knowing – known
   7. hear – heard – hearing – heard
   8. read – read – reading – read
   9. wear – wore – wearing – worn
   10. write – wrote – writing – written
   11. go – went – going – gone
   12. bite – bit – biting – bitten
   13. sing – sang – singing – sung

F. 1. were ; organize   2. arrived
   3. arrived ; had ; preparing
   4. felt   5. trained
   6. running   7. came ; placed
   8. ran   9. taking ; waiting
   10. finished

6 The Sentence

A. 1. John | watched a movie with his friends.
   2. The tired travellers | waited at the bus terminal.
   3. Most swimmers | fear the presence of sharks.
   4. Canada | is the largest country in the world.
   5. He | will take his bicycle with him on holiday.
   6. It | is a beautiful day today.

B. (Suggested answers)
   1. The horses and cows shared the barn.
   2. She laughed and cried at the same time.
   3. Red, blue, and yellow are her favourite colours.
   4. He chewed, swallowed, and digested his food.
   5. The girls and boys packed and carried the boxes.
   6. Joanna or Maria will babysit tonight.
   7. Janet washed and dried the clothes this morning.
   8. I can see some hens and ducks over there.

C. 1. has   2. like   3. wants   4. are
   5. were   6. play   7. are

D. (Answers may vary.)
   1. School was cancelled so the students went home.
   2. It was her birthday and she opened her presents.
   3. The weather was awful but we played outside anyway.
   4. We would be rewarded with treats if we did all our work.
   5. The fishermen waited patiently but they didn't catch a thing.
   6. They will be late if they miss the train.
   7. The children played a vigorous game of soccer so they were all very tired.
   8. The boys were hungry but there was nothing for them to eat.

E. (Answers will vary.)

7 Building Sentences with Descriptors

A. 1. French ; quietly   2. vicious ; fiercely
   3. puffy ; lazily   4. hot ; mercilessly
   5. young ; gracefully   6. reckless ; dangerously
   7. brave ; fearlessly   8. best ; kindly

B. 1. in ; ADV   2. of ; ADJ   3. of ; ADJ
   4. with ; ADJ   5. in ; ADJ   6. over ; ADV
   7. of ; ADJ   8. from ; ADJ   9. at ; ADV
   10. in ; ADV

C. 1. across the field ; over the hill
   2. In the summertime ; by a small lake
   3. in the textbook
   4. At the beginning ; of our gym class
   5. in front ; of the class
   6. in the gymnasium
   7. under our desks ; during the test
   8. (no phrase) ; "when the rain came down" is a clause
   9. in the house ; in the doghouse
   10. in the clearing ; on the campfire

D. (Individual writing)
Challenge
   (Answers will vary.)

Progress Test 1

A. 1. sidewalk ; walker   2. sadness ; happiness
   3. afternoon ; morning   4. children ; infant ; child
   5. stranger

B. 1. Mount Everest
   2. John
   3. June ; July

4. Ottawa ; Ottawa River
5. Disneyland
6. The Toronto Maple Leafs ; NHL

C. 1. ox   2. mice   3. fishes / fish
   4. child   5. wives   6. lives
   7. teeth   8. foot

D. 1. I – my / mine – we – our / ours
   2. she – her / hers – they – their / theirs
   3. it – its – they – their / theirs
   4. you – your / yours – you – your / yours

E. 1. beautiful   2. weary
   3. careful ; careless   4. large ; big ; enormous
   5. golden   6. precious ; valuable

F. 1. c   2. a   3. a   4. c
   5. a

G. 1. happily   2. carelessly   3. quickly
   4. creatively   5. finally

H. 1. chased ; picked   2. poured
   3. laughed ; wasn't   4. ate ; drank
   5. are

I. 1. play – I
   2. chose – T ; would wear – I
   3. gave – T
   4. was speaking – I ; listened – I
   5. covered – T ; blew – I

J. 1. were   2. had   3. could
   4. must   5. will

K. 1. drew   2. saw   3. caught
   4. wrote   5. thought   6. read
   7. drove   8. had   9. did
   10. cried

L. 1. The team | played football in the old stadium beside the river.
   2. Both the boys and the girls | used the same playing field during recess.
   3. The audience | laughed when they watched the funny movie.
   4. We | wear our gloves whenever it gets very cold.
   5. The tall boys | played basketball after school.
   6. It | rains whenever we plan a picnic.

M. (Suggested answers)
   1. Mike and Janet sang and laughed.
   2. We ate peanuts and popcorn at the baseball game.
   3. We laughed and cried at the same time.
   4. They created and presented the project together.
   5. The children jumped and splashed in the water.

N. 1. wants / wanted   2. enjoy ; enjoyed
   3. carry ; carried   4. go
   5. giggles ; is / giggled ; was
   6. drive ; drove   7. makes / made
   8. takes / took

O. 1. of the house – ADJ ; in the morning – ADV
   2. Outside the window – ADV ; on a branch – ADV
   3. In the evening – ADV ; for a drive – ADV ; to town – ADJ
   4. in the parking lot – ADJ
   5. of grade four – ADJ ; in the gymnasium – ADV

6. At the bottom – ADV ; of the pool – ADJ ; of the polo player – ADJ

P. 1. Swimming – G
   2. Hiking in the mountains – VP
   3. Looking in store windows – VP ; spending money – VP
   4. Singing – G ; dancing – G
   5. walking in the rain – VP
   6. Skiing – G ; tobogganing down the hills – VP

8 Prepositions and Conjunctions

A. 2. under   3. down   4. during
   5. across   6. of   7. between
   8. near   9. without   10. inside ; for

B. (Individual writing)

C. 2. in the sky – ADJ
   3. of the team – ADJ
   4. over the doorway – ADJ
   5. in the choir – ADV
   6. around the track – ADV
   7. Since yesterday – ADV
   8. for the school team – ADV
   9. throughout the house – ADV ; for her jacket – ADV
   10. of grade four – ADJ
   11. since yesterday – ADV

D. (Answers will vary.)

E. (Answers will vary.)

F. (Suggested answers)
   1. Unless you can show me a better way, I will do it my own way.
   2. Because she was the oldest, she made all the rules.
   3. We played the entire game even though we were very tired.
   4. If you are sure this is the right way to go, we will follow you.
   5. While I was talking on the phone, Sophia was watching a cartoon.

Challenge
(Suggested answers)
   1. Baseball is a great summer game.
   2. I caught a fish while I was sleeping in the boat.
   3. A needle in a haystack is hard to find.

9 Building Complex Sentences

A. 1. dependent   2. dependent   3. independent
   4. dependent   5. independent   6. independent
   7. dependent   8. independent   9. dependent
   10. dependent

B. 1. Whenever we go to the movies, we buy popcorn.
   2. She told us to wait until we all finished our homework.
   3. If the weather is clear, we can have a barbecue.
   4. After we watch our favourite television show, we go right to bed.
   5. Once the bell rings, recess is over.
   6. He is happy now that his bike is fixed.

7. As long as we live close by, <u>we can walk to school</u>.
8. <u>The students practised running</u> when it was track and field season.
9. Because she was late for class, <u>she had to go to the office first</u>.
10. <u>My father was looking forward to the holidays</u> because he could take time off work.

C. (Answers will vary.)

Challenge

(Suggested answers)
1. We went back to school because it was Monday.
2. The school play was cancelled when most of the participants were taken ill.
3. After the rain ended, the sun came out.
4. We waited for hours until the bus finally came.
5. The postman brought the mail when it was nearly noon hour.
6. We began to do our work after the morning announcements were made.
7. We get very tired whenever we have basketball practice.
8. If we are allowed, we will go to the game after school.

D. 1. Skiing – subject   2. biking – object
    3. eating – object   4. swimming – object

E. 1. skiing down the hill   2. Playing with the toys
    3. Listening to music

10   Relative Clauses

A. 1. who were located on the lower floor
2. where we used to play hide-and-seek
3. that are no longer used
4. that are facing extinction
5. whose children took the school bus
6. who scored the highest results in the test

B. (Individual writing)
C. (Individual writing)
D. (Individual writing)

E. 1. The dog, <u>which had a fluffy white coat</u>, played in the park.
2. His friend, <u>who was very reliable</u>, joined in the games they were playing.
3. The student, <u>who wore a green coat</u>, stood in the cold waiting for the school bus.
4. Relatives, <u>many of whom I didn't recognize</u>, arrived from everywhere.
5. Her friend, <u>who lives on the same street</u>, went away for the holidays.
6. Discussions about the environment, <u>which we enjoy</u>, are usually interesting.
7. The vacation, <u>which came in March</u>, gave us a much needed break from school.
8. Students, <u>who were carrying their knapsacks</u>, hurried into the school.
9. The boy, <u>who was riding a bicycle</u>, stopped at the store to make a purchase.

F. (Individual writing)
G. (Individual writing)

11   Developing the Paragraph

A. Titles (Answers will vary.)
Topic sentences :
1. Lauren's birthday present was a fluffy, little pup.
2. This summer, we will travel across Canada.
3. With two out in the ninth inning, we were losing by one run.
4. Kara had kept her birthday a secret from everyone at school except her best friend.

B. 1. D ; C ; A ; B   2. B ; C ; A ; D
   3. B ; C ; A ; D

C. (Individual writing)

12   Rules of Punctuation

A. 1. Incorrect – Look out!
2. Incorrect – I wondered why they hadn't arrived yet.
3. Correct
4. Correct
5. Incorrect – Never swim without supervision.
6. Incorrect – Ouch, that hurts!

B. 1. Mr.   2. US / U.S.   3. Ms.   4. p.m.
   5. Dr.   6. a.m.   7. B.C.   8. P.E.I.
   9. Nfld.   10. Co.

C.   Monday after school, we played basketball for the city championship. Our coach, Mr. Phillips, said, "I want everyone to try their hardest today." When the referee threw up the jump ball, the game had started. They missed their first shot, and we took the ball the length of the court for our first score. We knew that if we didn't play defence, we would lose. Each of us covered our man, and we allowed them to score very few baskets. The spectators cheered, screamed, clapped, and waved their arms during the game. Oddly enough, the opposition managed to even the score in the last minute of play. The championship came down to the last play of the game, and we had the ball.

  Slowly, carefully, and with great care, we brought the ball up the floor. Jamie, our team captain, called a time-out. We huddled around our coach and he said, "Make sure the last shot is a good one." Jamie, on a pass from Rick, dribbled to the corner, spun around, and threw up a rather long shot. The coach was not happy when this happened. But much to our surprise, the next sound we heard was "Swish".

D. 1. a. wasn't   b. I'll   c. won't
       d. he's   e. didn't   f. it's
       g. can't   h. isn't   i. I'm
       j. don't
   2. a. '62   b. '02   c. '95
   3. a. 1950's   b. p's and q's   c. 5's
   4. a. Paul's   b. team's   c. boy's
       d. women's   e. Ross's   f. doctors'

E. 1. "When are you going on holiday?" asked my friend, Lucy.
2. We watched "Malcolm in the Middle" last night on television.
3. Linda said, "I'll be home late tonight."

4. The teacher read an article from a magazine entitled "Getting Better Marks in School".
5. My family went to see "The Lion King" and heard the cast sing "The Lion Sleeps Tonight".
6. My father always sings his favourite song, "All You Need Is Love".
7. "Do you want to put on a skit in front of the class?" asked Antoinetta.
8. It could be titled "A Day in the Life of a Grade Four Student" as she suggested.
9. "The Man with Two Faces" is one of Joanna's favourite chapters in the Harry Potter book, *Harry Potter and the Philosopher's Stone*.
10. Lauren and Dayna sang "Happy Birthday to You" to their friend, Victoria, at her surprise birthday party.

13 Punctuation, Capitalization, and Abbreviations

A. 1. The final minute of the game was exciting; the score was tied.
2. Paul was an excellent artist; his paintings were hung in the hallway.
3. Rain poured down for most of the morning; the ground was too soggy for a soccer game.
4. The fire alarm sounded; luckily, it was only a drill.
5. His new bicycle was stolen; the police said they would look for it.
6. The science test was scheduled for Friday; therefore, I studied for most of Thursday night.
B. 1. Danny plays many sports: basketball, tennis, soccer, and baseball.
2. The teacher has one request: all pupils complete their homework.
3. He had a great idea: to form a homework club.
4. You have to remember: never play with matches again.
5. She invited the following friends: Amanda, Olivia, Samantha, and Jessica.
6. Roger had one main goal: he wanted to win the scoring title.
7. Her parents asked her to do the following: empty the dishwasher, clean her room, and take out the garbage.
8. They brought their pets to school for one reason: show-and-tell.
Challenge
1. ;   2. ;   3. :   4. :
5. :
C. 1. My – 1
2. Boy Scouts – 5
3. Department of Transport – 5
4. Quebec City – 3
5. French ; German ; Italian – 6
6. Canada Day – 4
7. Montreal ; Quebec ; St. Lawrence River – 3
8. Canadian National Exhibition – 2

Challenge
1. ocean ; ships   2. north-east   3. company
D. 1. G   2. F   3. D   4. A
5. C   6. B   7. H   8. K
9. E   10. I   11. J   12. L
Challenge
1. Royal Canadian Mounted Police
2. Mountain   3. Junior
4. Avenue   5. Television
6. as soon as possible

14 Tips for Effective Writing

A. (Suggested answers)
1. V – The store owner closed up the shop early.
2. V – Paul sprinted across the field to get the ball.
3. S – I looked everywhere for my missing cat.
4. V – She walked down the street in the rain.
5. S and V – He worked to earn extra money to buy a new bike.
B. 1. was – were / are
2. are – is
3. want – wants
4. is – are / were
5. plays – play / played
6. walk – walks
7. dance – dances / danced
8. thrown – threw
C. (Suggested answers)
1. It was raining hard in the morning.
2. The game began on time in the afternoon. / The afternoon game began on time.
3. We had free, delicious pizza for lunch.
4. We stood in a line up to see the first *Harry Potter* movie.
5. We ran, jumped, and skipped acrooss the schoolyard.
D. 1. My friend said, "The movie began at two o'clock."
2. We brought cookies, cakes, buns, and pies to the bake sale.
3. I don't like trying to do things that I can't do.
4. She doesn't like waiting in line at the show to buy popcorn, candy, pop, and ice cream.
5. Whenever we go shopping, we always spend too much money.
6. I will be able to stay over at your house if I finish cleaning my room.
E. 1. It's   2. our ; way
3. know ; which ; fair   4. too
5. plane ; plain   6. dye ; die
7. brake ; bear   8. Whose
F. 1. wasn't ; ever / was ; never
2. hasn't ; any / has ; no
3. didn't ; any
4. didn't ; anybody ; were
5. didn't ; anyone / told ; no one

15 Writing Descriptive and Narrative Paragraphs

A. (Answers will vary.)
B. (Answers will vary.)
C. (Individual writing)
D. (Individual writing)

Progress Test 2

A. 1. for ; in   2. under
    3. of   4. but
    5. until   6. with
    7. and ; or   8. over
B. 1. ADV   2. ADJ   3. ADV ; ADV
    4. ADV   5. ADV   6. ADJ
    7. ADJ   8. ADV
C. (Individual writing)
D. (Suggested answers)
    1. After we ate dinner, we watched television.
    2. Since I got a flat tire, I haven't been able to ride my bicycle.
    3. Although I slept in until noon, I was still tired.
    4. Whenever we have a picnic, it always rains.
    5. We couldn't go to the park because we didn't have a ride.
    6. We waited all day long until the bus arrived.
E. 1. complex   2. compound   3. complex
    4. complex   5. compound   6. compound
    7. compound
F. 1. Running – subject   2. dancing – object
    3. writing – object   4. Laughing – subject
    5. Swimming – subject   6. Playing – subject
    7. skiing – subject
G. 1. C   2. G   3. F   4. E
    5. H   6. B   7. D   8. A
H. 1. The grade four class memorized the poem "The Vagabond Song" by Bliss Carmen.
    2. "Scooby Doo" is a very popular children's television show.
    3. Shakespeare wrote the famous play "Romeo and Juliet".
    4. His father said, "Do not forget to take your house key with you."
    5. "What time will the movie end?" she asked.
    6. "Gulliver's Travels" is one of my favourite stories.
    7. "Think carefully before you make the decision," the teacher reminded her.
    8. One critic stated that the first "Harry Potter" book was a terrific read and a stunning first novel.
I. 1. ;   2. :   3. :
    4. ;   5. ;   6. :

J. On Canada Day, we went to Ottawa for the celebration. There were lots of people outside the Parliament Buildings. Although we were not able to get to the front, we could get a good view of the stage. The performance was superb, and everyone had a good time. "Do you want to stay for the firework display?" my father asked us. "Of course!" we all responded excitedly.
K. 1. which happened to fall on February 29 ; NR
    2. that was needed to do the job ; R
    3. who was exhausted from the race ; R
    4. who has been on staff for many years ; NR
    5. whose name was Scamp ; NR
    6. which I gave Sam for his birthday ; NR
    7. whom everyone likes ; NR
    8. who care ; R
L. (Suggested answers)
    1. We would stay at the room that was small but tidy for the night.
    2. I like the backpack which my mom bought for my tenth birthday.
    3. The game, which lasted more than four hours, was boring.
    4. The boy whom we called The Joker was funny.
    5. The tall structure which stands next to the SkyDome is the CN Tower.

1 Seal Island

A. 1. feed 2. meat-eaters
3. hidden 4. trap
5. leaping 6. surprised
7. throwing

B. (Any 4)
1. safety ; shore ; squids ; schools ; small ; stalking ; seals ; sound ; surface ; September ; south ; surrounding ; shark ; spectacular ; swimming
2. main ; migrate ; makes ; months ; making ; move ; meal
3. cape ; crabs ; cooler ; carnivores ; can ; camouflaged ; capture
4. perfect ; peril ; predator ; prey

C. 1. B ; flesh-eaters / meat-eaters ; sharks (Suggested answer) ; seals (Suggested answer)
2. A ; vegetable-eaters / plant-eaters ; horses (Suggested answer) ; cows (Suggested answer)
3. C ; meat- and plant-eaters ; human beings (Suggested answer) ; dogs (Suggested answer)

D. (Individual writing)

2 More than Candy

A. 1. appealed 2. strategy
3. assorted 4. dispenser
5. conventions 6. originally

B. (Individual answers)

C. 1. E 2. G 3. J
4. I 5. B 6. D
7. A 8. F 9. C
10. H

D. (Individual answers)
E. (Individual answers)
F. (Individual design)

3 The Surprise Holiday

A. (Individual writing)

B. 1. C 2. E 3. D
4. H 5. F 6. G
7. B 8. A

C. Two Syllables : drowsy ; purchased ; suitcase ; question
Three Syllables : expressions ; disbelief ; vacation ; reactions
Four Syllables : everyone ; destination ; activities ; reality

D. 1. chil-dren 2. air-plane
3. par-ents 4. ho-tel
5. beau-tiful ; beauti-ful 6. hol-iday ; holi-day
7. di-rections ; direc-tions
8. hap-piness ; happi-ness

E. (Individual answers)

F. LATW ; SIYDEN ; RLODW
G. WALT DISNEY WORLD

4 Hear Ye...Hear Ye! (Part 1)

A.

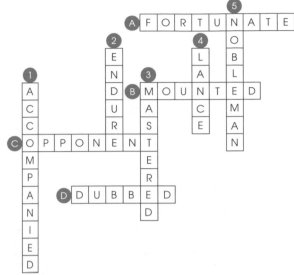

B. 1. please 2. greeting
3. teach 4. battlefield
5. cheer 6. dreamed
7. queen 8. brief
9. piece / peace 10. peace / piece
11. feelings 12. believed
13. leaving 14. needed
15. achieve

C. 1. friend ; Noblemen living in a castle
2. fighting ; About learning
3. servant ; For fighting
4. manners ; Skills a "page" had to learn
5. ceremony ; Traits needed to be a knight

D. "a" to "h" :
1. born 2. castle
3. ceremony 4. experiences
5. falcon 6. fighting
"i" to "p" :
1. knight 2. lady
3. lance 4. level
5. lord 6. manners
"q" to "z" :
1. riding 2. skills
3. stronger 4. taught
5. training 6. wrestling

E. (Individual writing)

5 Hear Ye...Hear Ye! (Part 2)

A. 1. E 2. D 3. G
4. I 5. C 6. A
7. J 8. B 9. H
10. F

B. (Individual writing)
C. 1. today   2. slave
    3. pain   4. faith
    5. saying   6. shame
    7. stayed   8. plate
    9. praise   10. away
    11. training   12. bathed
    13. awaited   14. grateful
    15. displayed
D. 1. knight   2. knife
    3. knee   4. knead
    5. knot   6. knew
    7. knuckle   8. know
    9. knelt
Challenge
    knowledge
E. decide – demand :
    defend ; defeat ; deem ; deliver ; declare
    lord – loyal :
    loser ; loud ; lovely ; lower ; lost
    feast – festival :
    feather ; feed ; feat ; fellow ; feel
    tradition – trait :
    tragic ; trail ; training ; traipse
F. 1. Edward studied many years to become a knight.
    2. Would you like to live during the Middle Ages?
    3. Tomorrow Edward will be dubbed by Lord Henry.

6   The Case of the Disappearing Fish

A. Heron
B. 1. seafood   2. someone
    3. sunrise   4. backyard
    5. suitable   6. something
    7. waterfall   8. outside
Challenge
    neighbourhood
C.

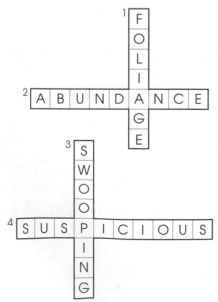

D. (Individual writing)
E. • Suburbs near Rattray Marsh
    • José's beautiful backyard
    • Mysterious or puzzling mood
    (Individual drawing)

7   Not a Typical Grandma

A. 1. C   2. B   3. C
    4. A   5. A   6. C
    7. B   8. A
B. B ; D ; E ; A ; C
C. "ou" words :
    1. sound   2. South
    3. outfits   4. mountain
    "ow" words :
    1. brown   2. down
D. 1. outside   2. flower
    3. crown   4. found
    5. flour   6. shout
    7. Mouse   8. cloudy
    9. Hound
Challenge
    allowance

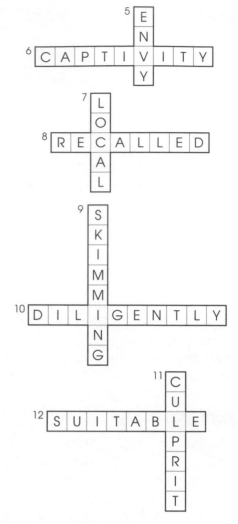

E. (Individual writing)

F. (Individual answers)

Progress Test 1

A. 1. c. ; l. 2. tbsp. ; ml.
   3. tsp. ; ml. 4. c. ; ml.
   5. c. ; ml. 6. c. ; ml.
   7. tbsp. ; ml. 9. lg. ; pkg.
   10. temp. ; F. ; C. ; min. ; dz. ; lg. ; dz. ; med.

B. Two Syllables : measure ; mixture ; flavour ; preheat
   Three Syllables : delicious ; tablespoon ; margarine ; appetite
   Four Syllables : temperature ; appetizer ; decoration ; ingredient

C. 1. meat-eater 2. jealous
   3. interested 4. neighbourhood
   5. meetings 6. judge
   7. mastery 8. clothing
   9. delicious 10. lived
   11. cleanse 12. forever
   13. plenty 14. feed
   15. diving 16. different

D. "a" to "h" :
   1. apron 2. chef
   3. cupcake 4. dessert
   5. eggs 6. grill
   "i" to "p" :
   1. icing 2. kitchen
   3. muffins 4. nuts
   5. oven 6. pastry
   "q" to "z" :
   1. recipe 2. serving
   3. snack 4. sprinkles
   5. tasty 6. utensil

E. 1. do-nuts 2. rai-sins
   3. car-amel ; cara-mel
   4. cin-namon ; cinna-mon
   5. choc-olate ; choco-late
   6. dec-orate ; deco-rate
   7. tem-perature ; temper-ature ; tempera-ture

F.

1. dish	melon	dishwasher
2. blue	scotch	blueberry
3. clean	holder	cleanup
4. water	spoon	watermelon
5. butter	fruit	butterscotch
6. tea	berry	teaspoon
7. pot	washer	potholder
8. grape	up	grapefruit

G. bagel – banana :
   baker ; ball ; balance

chef – chop :
chill ; chestnut ; cherry ; chip ; chocolate
flaky – flour :
flatten ; flavour ; flipper ; flatware ; flapjack
special – spray :
spoon ; spice ; sponge ; split ; spend

H. 1. T 2. S 3. T
   4. T 5. S 6. S

I. 1. B 2. C 3. A
   4. C 5. B 6. A
   7. B

J. 1. plate ; Silverware
   2. cake ; Baking ingredients
   3. candles ; Can be eaten
   4. yogurt ; Things that are baked
   5. brownies ; Types of cookies

K. long "a" sound :
   spray ; grain ; tasty (taste) ; tray ; scale
   long "e" sound :
   grease ; piece ; cream ; yield ; peel
   "ow" sound :
   flour ; paper towel ; ground ; brown ; pound

8 Being the Eldest

A. (Individual writing)

B. 1. secluded 2. quantities
   3. siblings 4. role model

C. 4 ; 5 ; 3

D. 1. advantage 2. young
   3. interest 4. total
   5. irritate 6. regard
   7. practise 8. quantity

E. Evan loved to climb in the attic where he had a secret hideaway. He kept his favourite toys and books up there. Evan also stored Christmas presents for his family in the attic. He made sure nobody followed him when he escaped to his hideout.

9 The Victory of Lance Armstrong

A. 1. D 2. J 3. E
   4. B 5. G 6. I
   7. A 8. C 9. H
   10. F

B. (Individual writing)

C. 1. triathlete ; an athlete that does three sports
   2. misread ; understood wrongly
   3. uncertain ; not sure
   4. dismounted ; got off
   5. prejudged ; judged before something really happened

D. 1. His bike ; a bolt of lightning
   2. The cyclist ; sizzling bacon

3. His mouth ; desert sand

E. (Individual answers)

10 A Rebus Invitation

A. Dear Stacey,

You are invited to my birthday party on Sunday, July 1st. It starts at 2 o'clock and ends at 5 o'clock. We will meet at the Wheeler Horse Farm on Queen Street.

Lunch will be hotdogs, french fries, and cupcakes. Please bring sunscreen and bug spray.

Your friend,
Shelley

B. (Individual answers)
C. (Individual answers)
D. (Individual writing)
E.
1. happiness
2. baker
3. dancing
4. thankless
5. excitable
6. wishful
7. decorator
8. fearless
9. usually
10. teachable
11. climbed
12. flavourful

11 A Sporty Gal

A. (Suggested answers)
1. However
2. Finally
3. before
4. After
5. As a result
6. As soon as
B. (Individual writing)
C.
1. basketball
2. The Olympic Games
D. (Suggested answers)
score : store ; restore ; more ; door ; roar
kick : tick ; click ; quick ; sick ; trick
speed : bleed ; deed ; weed ; seed ; read
goal : roll ; sole ; role ; coal ; pole
E. (Individual writing)

12 Cornfield Today, Volcano Tomorrow

A.
1. phone
2. afloat
3. overflow
4. soul
5. throw
6. though
7. bulldoze
8. close
9. grown
10. shadow
11. raincoat
12. dough
B.
1. pianist
2. machinist
3. scientist
4. geologist
5. violinist
6. florist
7. dentist
8. pharmacist
C.
1. rumbling
2. crack
3. whistling

D.
1. old windows on a windy day
2. eating potato chips
3. eating spaghetti
4. jumping in a pool
5. washing dishes
6. sound of a dog

splash
clang
crunch
bark
slurp
rattle

E. (Individual writing)
F.
1. B
2. A
3. A
4. B
G. (Individual writing)

13 Nature's Fireworks

A. (Definitions : Individual answers)
1. causing fear for being strange
2. send out
3. in or of times long ago
4. bright and strong, producing a sharp sensation on the eyes
5. very small pieces
6. something that causes wonder and admiration
7. sign that something is going to happen in the future
B. (Individual writing)
C. (Individual writing)
D. A ; B ; D
E. (Individual writing)

14 A Pet's Tale

A. C ; E ; A ; F ; D ; B
Challenge
A dog
B. (Individual answers)
(Individual writing)
C. (Individual answers)
Challenge
(Individual writing)
D.
1. sail
2. deer
3. plane
4. heel
5. bear
6. rain
7. pear
8. flower
E.
1. Their ; there
2. rode ; road
3. hole ; whole
4. hare ; hair
5. threw ; through
6. write ; right

15 Camp Wannastay

A.
1. C
2. E
3. F
4. A
5. B
6. D

B. 1. The concerned counsellor took a thorough look around for poison ivy.
2. We heard a startling noise and ran swiftly to our cabin.
3. Although my time at camp was brief, I had an enjoyable experience.
4. They gave generous portions of dessert and it was always scrumptious.
5. By the end of our lengthy hiking excursion, I felt extremely weary.

C. (Individual writing)

D. 1. bought   2. caught
   3. fought   4. brought
   5. thought   6. taught

E. 1. rough   2. laugh
   3. cough   4. trough
   5. tough

F. (Individual design)

Progress Test 2

A. 1. company   2. best
   3. clubhouse   4. groovy
   5. backyard   6. jokes
   7. relationship   8. strong

B. 1. un<u>success</u>ful   2. <u>frightful</u>
   3. dis<u>appear</u>   4. <u>end</u>less
   5. <u>wonder</u>ful   6. <u>performance</u>
   7. <u>friend</u>liest   8. <u>sudden</u>ly
   9. un<u>believ</u>able

C. 1. wondorful   2. performer
   3. novelist   4. thoughtless
   5. laughable   6. carefully
   7. sailor   8. happiness

D. 1. bored   2. cent
   3. there   4. ware / wear
   5. bean   6. new
   7. threw   8. eye
   9. ours   10. eight

E. Sight : bright ; blurry ; shiny
Sound : crackling ; whistling ; swishing
Smell : rotten ; skunky ; fruity
Taste : spicy ; bitter ; tangy
Touch : silky ; squishy ; fuzzy

F. 1. We practised our dance moves until we mastered them.
2. Madison and Nicole attended each other's parties.
3. We studied many school subjects together.

G.   Madison and Nicole keep themselves busy when they're together. <u>First</u>, they disappear into the clubhouse for a game of cards. <u>Then</u>, they check out the fridge for snacks and drinks. <u>After</u> their snack break, Nicole and Madison listen to music. <u>Before</u> they head out to the backyard, they play a board game

or two. <u>Finally</u>, they settle in for secrets on the hammock.

H. 1. swift ; fast   2. many ; numerous
   3. start ; initiate   4. oldest ; eldest
   5. pester ; annoy   6. short ; brief
   7. victory ; win   8. ruckus ; noisy
   9. vivid ; bright   10. marvel ; wonder

I. 1. frightened   2. excited
   3. sad   4. happy
   5. angry / frustrated

J. 1. chirping   2. boom
   3. popped   4. clanged
   5. buzzed

K. 1. mis ; understand something wrongly
   2. dis ; oppose
   3. mid ; middle of the night
   4. tri ; three colours
   5. pre ; plan in advance
   6. un ; open

L. 1. E   2. F
   3. G   4. A
   5. C   6. B
   7. D

M. 1. C   2. C
   3. C ; D ; A ; B

1. I HAVE HAD GREAT FUN HERE AND I WILL VISIT YOU AGAIN NEXT YEAR.

2.

mice → mine → mint → mist

coin → corn → born → burn

3.

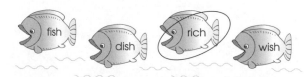

fish   dish   (rich)   wish

duck   tuck   luck   (back)

star   jar   (for)   car

(lock)   look   book   hook

share   bear   pear   (dear)

4.

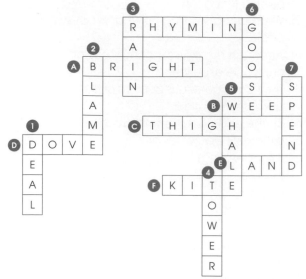

Crossword:

- 3 down / across: R H Y M I N G
- 2: R A I N (RAIN going down)
- A: B R I G H T
- 6: G O O S E
- L A M   (ALARM down)
- 5: O S S   1: D E A L
- B: W E E P
- C: T H I G H
- D: D O V E
- 7: S P E N
- E: L A N D
- F: K I T E
- 4: T O W E R

5.

cone → tone → tune → tube

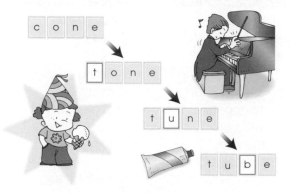

sail → tail → tall → tell

6.

I	D	j	f	n	D	A	u	g	u	s	t
F	e	O	A	J	h	e	O	l	e	i	d
j	c	b	c	M	a	r	c	h	k	u	N
S	e	J	J	t	N	n	c	S	F	o	h
A	m	g	u	D	o	a	u	M	e	J	k
h	b	M	l	n	v	b	s	a	b	t	a
m	e	o	y	F	e	N	e	y	r	s	y
s	r	e	m	V	m	b	w	r	u	y	n
O	b	J	i	O	b	e	M	g	a	z	k
n	S	e	p	t	e	m	b	e	r	x	p
j	a	k	A	p	r	i	l	c	y	d	r
c	e	o	M	g	D	f	d	i	l	m	e

7.
1. STEAL
2. THINK
3. SCARCE
4. SEAT
5. CHIEF
6. FLIGHT
7. GRAIN
8. EXIST / EXITS
9. SWING
10. TUBE
11. REPLY
12. BOAT

8.

rose → rise → rice → dice

near → neat → beat → bean

9.

ELVES OXEN
CITIES
HEROES
CHILDREN
MESOOMRE

10.

A. STARE
B. IIER
C. MOUSSE
D. STEALS
E. EYES
F. KNOW

11.

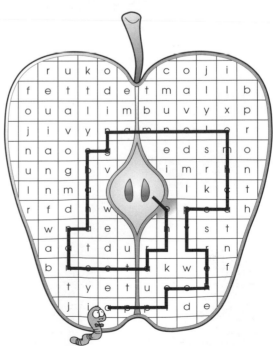

12.

wise → wide → wine → wind

belt → bell → well → wall

15.

road → roar → rear → near

bear → bead → head → heat

13. 1. EAR ; PEA ; PAR ; PER ; ERA
2. EEL ; LET ; BET ; BEE ; TEE
3. GEM ; TEN ; MEN ; NET ; MET
4. HIS ; HIT ; SIT ; ITS ; SIR

14. 1. Kangaroo   2. alien
3. statue   4. hammer
5. fork   6. turtle
7. toboggan   8. envelope
9. video game

16.

c	e	g	y	p	k	d	c	i	m	f	g
f	j	p	m	u	s	h	r	o	o	m	o
a	a	d	o	m	b	g	c	h	r	b	k
i	n	r	q	p	r	r	m	a	w	n	e
l	t	u	t	k	o	n	i	o	n	i	g
a	o	d	r	i	c	j	o	t	r	n	g
c	m	s	n	n	c	p	y	b	a	k	p
e	a	j	c	g	o	h	v	x	t	e	l
l	t	r	t	b	l	u	o	z	b	h	a
e	o	l	r	d	i	l	s	k	e	q	n
r	h	e	p	o	t	a	t	o	e	i	t
y	b	p	j	s	t	m	u	s	t	e	b